THE MOTHER-LOVING GUIDE

Truths about life with a newborn and
how to prepare (a little)

Silke Thistlewood founded her business — 'Raise Up Mums' — in 2018 after her own struggle with postnatal depression and anxiety, and being unable to find suitable well-being resources for mothers. She supports women as they adjust to motherhood (an often overlooked and underestimated transition) with realistic self-care and resilience tools, and an online community. She's passionate about mothers receiving more support during the early years of parenting, which this book forms a major part of.

Silke is also a massage therapist of 12 years, with a focus on pre- and postnatal treatments, including scar massage for C-sections.

In her spare time, which she's able to negotiate more and more expertly nowadays, she loves submerging in open water and lifting heavy things, preferably over her head. Silke lives with her husband and two daughters in Kent, waiting with bated breath to adopt a rescue dog, after losing their 'practice baby' chocolate lab after 13 years.

For Megan, Ellie and Andy

SILKE THISTLEWOOD

THE MOTHER -LOVING GUIDE

Truths about life
with a newborn & how
to prepare (A LITTLE)

A CIP catalogue record for this title is available from the British Library.

Paperback ISBN: 978-1-7396218-0-3
eBook ISBN: 978-1-7396218-1-0

Editor Julia Kellaway
Proofreader Andie Coupland
Art Director and Designer Em Williams

Typeset in Quincy CF by lettersbyem.studio

Ordering Information:
For details, contact *silke@raiseupmums.co.uk*.

https://www.raiseupmums.co.uk/

CONTENTS

FOREWORD

BY SOPHIE BURCH ('The Mamma Coach')

Any book with a title that includes the words 'mother-loving' is a welcome addition to my bookshelf, and this thoughtful, compassionate and practical little book has not disappointed! Silke has put her experience, wisdom and understanding of early motherhood into every page, and each section will resonate deeply with parents and people in pregnancy everywhere.

Silke's tone is comforting, personal and realistic, with no gloss – a welcome breath of fresh air in a business that often forces top tips and perfection into vulnerable, tired parents' hands and minds with too much ferocity and ease. This book brims with practical advice and explains how to apply it and why it can be useful. It helps the reader to make sense of their experiences, understand themselves better, as well as their close relationships. The mere mention of 'relationships' in this book brings relief to my mind, as it's often the elephant in the room when it comes to bringing a baby into our arms – and is one of the biggest reasons parents struggle. The other elephant in the room is, naturally (or not), SLEEP. Silke touches gently and soothingly on this rather *huge* issue for new parents with knowledge, empathy and expertise.

Silke's guide is quick, easy to digest, fun to read and insightful. In my view, she's got it covered: mind, body, baby, bonding, mental health and more! The fact that there's a whole chapter dedicated to unpacking guilt and another to comparison is the icing on the cake. These are emotive topics that no new mother can escape or ignore, so we'd better settle in and work out some ways of dealing with them, with compassion, reflection and recognition.

Silke writes like a wise, experienced older sibling who truly cares. You want to listen. You know you are held and feel you can trust in her knowledge.

INTRODUCTION

When I was pregnant with my first child – and, in fact, even before that – motherhood felt like a secret club that was being kept very, very quiet indeed. No one told me about it honestly until I became a mum. Then, all of a sudden, people shared their experiences and strangers stopped me in the park to check how much sleep I was getting and if I was OK.

I don't want it to feel like that for new mums anymore. I want there to be honesty, kindness and a chance to prepare (as much as that's possible because you really don't *quite* know what it will be like until you're actually living it). And that's why I've written this book – to provide honest information along with realistic and practical ways to prepare that go beyond birth, pushchairs, nappy brands and nursery decoration. I want to take the fear out of the unknown by lifting the lid on life with a baby, not to scare you, but so that you're not taken by surprise to the degree that I was (and many others, as I've found out through my research). Knowing how much I would have appreciated a simple 'By the way, it will feel hard sometimes, but that's normal', I can't wait to provide that reassurance for you. And just a warning – there'll be many a bad joke along the way to lighten the mood; I make no apology for this.

Dotted throughout are also some soundbites from my 'Raise Up Mums' community and mothers from further afield in answer to the question 'What do you wish you'd known before having your first child?' I put out a survey and, in their hundreds, mums poured out their thoughts, experiences and virtual hugs to you reading this now, in preparation for motherhood. On my website (www.raiseupmums.co.uk) you'll also find some letters mums have written to their pregnant selves – a form of therapy for both them and you!

I remember asking the antenatal class teacher towards the end of our sessions what we'd actually *do* once we brought the baby home. We hadn't covered anything post-birth, except breastfeeding, by this point (turns out that we never would…) and I couldn't understand why. Her answer took the form of a laugh and a flippant 'You'll put the car seat with the baby in it on the table, boil the kettle and wonder what on earth you've done.' Helpful? No. Accurate? Somewhat.

When I questioned this at a post-birth meet-up, she answered that pregnant women simply aren't ready to take in the realities of what early motherhood can be like. This raised my hackles — I had specifically asked and had wanted to know, yet I received no information, no heads-up, no reassurance and no support.

Friends who'd already had kids fell in a similar category. I never outright asked them what being a mother was like, but I assumed it couldn't be all that bad, because I'd never heard anything to the contrary. But then I discovered that everyone just keeps shtum until you're in, and then they let rip with concern, honesty, advice and horror stories galore.

I really hope this book will prepare you in lots of little, practical ways for what's to come and go some way towards working against the societal norms and expectations that have been placed on the motherhood experience (or that we've placed on ourselves). I want you to feel held, supported and guided, but at the same time armed with knowledge and information you can draw on in times of need.

A LITTLE ABOUT ME

I'm a mum of two girls (at the time of writing, they are five and nine years old), and I'll happily admit to anyone that I'm not a fan of the baby phase. I remember the physical sense of relief when I heard a mum share this when my eldest was around three years old. I'd never heard anyone admit this before and remember thinking, 'I didn't know this was an option!' Give me a tantruming toddler or a back-talking six-year-old any day — babies terrify me. I didn't feel a proper bond with my first until well into her second year. That connection steadily grew from around six months onwards (thank goodness, because it's exhausting feeling so scared all the time!) and by the time she was two-and-a-half we were such a team.

I knew a little more what to expect the second time round, but I found it difficult to meet the new baby's needs around the existing kid. Through all of this, my always-present anxiety intensified and I found it increasingly difficult to look after myself. Searches for resources left me empty-handed (luckily that's changed a lot now!), which led me to set up Raise Up Mums, a Facebook community where I aim to smooth the transition into motherhood for women through sharing the ups and downs of motherhood honestly. I wanted to share those things that were helping me feel better about myself and in motherhood — oodles of self-compassion and self-kindness (acknowledging that motherhood is actually hard and that we're never alone in feeling this way), consistent self-care (and working on not feeling guilty for putting ourselves first sometimes) and creating a non-judgemental community where belonging and support are at the forefront.

The Raise Up Mums community now has over 1,200 members and, through conversations in the groups, workshops and courses I've run, the same topics come up over and over again: overwhelm, guilt, the juggle of it all, not having enough help and feeling like we're not doing motherhood 'right' if we're not enjoying every minute. My hope is that this book will reach some parents-to-be in time to pre-empt and squash some of these concerns before they have a chance to pop up. Or at the very least prepare them for when they do!

HOW TO USE THIS BOOK

> *'There is no right or wrong way. Do what works for you and your child/family.'*

Before having my first child, I was really concerned that I hadn't read enough books and didn't know enough about infant care. I then made up for that by reading *all* of them once the baby was born. I read about routines, stages of development and so many books on sleep. But all they did was overwhelm me with information and give me more things to potentially feel guilty about.

And, yes, I totally get how ironic it is that I've now written my own 'parenting book', BUT it's different! (It actually is!) At no point will I tell you what to do. I'll merely make suggestions based on my own experiences and those of other mums I've encountered along the way, offering ways in which you can think about your own situation and use that as a starting point for laying the foundations for how you can best support yourself in the first few years of parenting. I actively encourage you to ignore the bits that you don't think apply to you and only take away what resonates and seems helpful — a disclaimer I think every parenting book should come with.

The main aim of this book is to prepare you for having your first baby, but it will be useful wherever you are in your motherhood journey. I say 'motherhood' journey, rather than 'parenting' journey, because I feel that a lot of the worries and overwhelm of parenting are unique to mothers. That's not to say that reading this book won't be helpful for other parenting partners; in fact, many of the preparation exercises are designed to be done as a couple, but a lot of the physical and emotional strain is specific to mums. It's very, very helpful indeed for parenting partners to be aware of all of these strains in order to offer better support and understanding, but the book itself is geared towards mothers for this reason.

Each chapter spotlights a different topic, such as supporting your mental health, asking for help in the early days and accepting your ever-changing body, and aims to prepare you for the practicalities of living with a newborn. There is space to make notes and prompts throughout for you to think about your situation and how you can best put some preparations in place, as well as a little directory at the end of the book to complete (see page 144). Ideally you'd do this before baby arrives, so that you'll have everything already thought through and noted down when you actually need it. But, of course, you can go through these resources any time after giving birth – all in your own time. While it's tempting to skip these parts of the book (I get it – I've ignored many a worksheet or exercise!), I would like to nudge you lovingly towards completing them. Even just reading through the questions, might prompt some 'huh, I didn't think of that' moments that will mean a smoother transition into motherhood. And that's worth a lot.

To break up my ramblings, and to include a variety of voices, you'll find lots of quotes dotted through the book, along with some of my favourite parenting mantras that have kept me going through the long nights and repetitive days. I've also asked some of my friends, who just happen to be experts in various postnatal spaces, to add their thoughts and knowledge in specific 'Expert Voice' sections throughout.

Experiences shared are overwhelmingly from mothers in relationships and birth mothers, but I very much hope that they apply universally and that you're able to take away useful information no matter your parental circumstances. Whether you arrived in motherhood through surrogacy or adoption, are a single or LGBTQ+ mother, the common threads and strains of motherhood are universal. While we don't all have the same resources and circumstances, we can still relate and empathise with each other and we could all use more help, support and belonging.

In a nutshell, take in what you can and leave what seems too much or unimportant for another time. There's a lot of information here and I know that it can seem overwhelming, so know that you don't have to read it all now. Come back to it whenever you need to and redo the planning pages whenever you feel there's been a shift in your life.

Please enjoy and don't let any of it frighten you – I'm here for you every step of the way.

CHAPTER 1

ASKING FOR HELP

It really does take a village to raise a child.

You can assemble your own village that doesn't need to be compiled of family.

In hindsight, I wish we'd moved closer to my in-laws. We did what so many people do and moved house while I was pregnant with our first (hey, maybe that's you right now!). We could have moved anywhere, but decided against moving too near my husband's folks for whatever reason at the time and I often wish now that they were half an hour down the road!

Because sometimes clichés are true — **we really weren't meant to do this alone**. The saying is 'it takes a village to raise a child' for a very good reason, because that's exactly what used to happen. Extended family and neighbours held the baby while the mum slept, showered, ate, chatted to other grown-ups without interruptions... the list goes on.

Instead, these days, we're being told through all available channels that we can, and possibly should, do it all. On our own. While we smile and look pretty. And when we can't (because we're not robots and actual life doesn't come with a filter), we feel like we've failed. <Steps off soap box to calm down.>

If you're lucky enough to have family close by who you get on with and who you actually want around to help you, I'll talk you through how to get them on board and organised for lending a hand. And, of course, all is not lost if you don't have relatives around to help. It's possible to widen your support network, or create a new one from scratch, to get the help you need. I'll walk you through that, too.

If at this point you're struggling to visualise why you might need the level of help I'm hinting at here (I totally get it — I felt the same), imagine for a minute that you've broken your leg and are struggling to get up, let alone make it up the stairs or out of the house. What sort of things would you rope people in to help you with? Chores, cooking, shopping, phone calls for entertainment and light relief? That's the kind of help you're also looking for in the first few months of motherhood. Start getting a mental list going of who you might want to call on and we'll get it all on paper soon.

Before we move on to practicalities, let's nip this old chestnut in the bud: Asking for help is a sign of weakness. We've already established that bringing up kids is really not meant to happen in isolation. You're not weak for not wanting to/not being able to soldier through sleep deprivation and postnatal healing. Asking for support is going to enable you to enjoy motherhood and maybe even some slices of your 'old life' here and there. **You're setting yourself up for long-term success and well-being by asking for, and accepting, help.** So let's get to it!

Below is a little guide around how to go about it, and there is a planning space on page 21 to complete to help you to get people lined up and confirmed now.

HOW TO ASK FOR HELP

First of all, people love to help. It feels good to help others, right? Who are you to deny people feeling good about themselves? I joke, but it's also true. We think we're wildly inconveniencing people when we reach out, but it might just put a spring in their step.

Anyone who's already had kids will be falling over themselves to help you, because they've been there. Let them. They're keen *and* they know what they're doing. One of my neighbours had slightly older kids and she volunteered to push my baby round the park for her nap so I could rest. My neighbour loved it because she missed having a tiny baby, I loved it because I got some space and time to myself, and baby loved it because she got to have a nap in the fresh air (and on the move – her favourite!). As a result, I was a more patient and fun mum on her return, so everyone had a better day for accepting the help.

BE SPECIFIC

Just declaring you need something won't do. It won't magically happen. Spell it out, make it as specific as you can and repeat it until it happens.

I used to say to my husband, 'I really need a bath this weekend, I'm so achey.' But it never happened. Not because my husband's a horrible man who denies me a soothing bath, but because he found it impossible to work out when in the day might have worked best (and if he suggested a time I *may* have barked at him on more than one occasion that he clearly wasn't across the baby's nap and food schedules... we'll touch on postnatal anger a little later!).

I think we all fantasise about someone simply guessing what we need and then just making it happen, but that's not very realistic. Or at least not all the time. Once I started saying, 'Can you feed the baby dinner tonight so I can have a bath in peace?', it started happening. Makes sense, right? It can be so very hard to get over ourselves to ask for what we need, when we need it, but it gets easier with practice and it's one of motherhood's great necessities.

Maybe you'd love to catch up on some sleep every now and again. How about asking to take it in turns to get up with baby at the weekends? (Or for you to go back to bed once you've breastfed.) Maybe you miss spending time with your friends. Could your partner push the pram round the park for an hour while you grab a coffee? Or if a friend also has a baby, the other halves could bond while they push the prams and you get to chat in peace.

It's also really helpful to add why you're asking for something: 'I haven't felt like myself lately and would love to restart an old hobby. I've found a choir that practices on Friday nights. Could you make sure you finish work on time to take the bath and bedtime shift so I can go please?' I mean, how could anyone say no? My personal challenge with this is not to let it get to a point where I'm so desperate that my plea for help becomes an overly emotional blame fest ('I never have any time for myself to do the things I like doing because you come home so late and I'm at the end of my tether'), so it pays to ask well before you hit that totally exhausted, angry zone.

'It's OK to ask for help more than once.'

'Set out expectations for household responsibilities, baby care and self-care before the baby arrives so that everyone knows which job is whose.'

'Ask for help. Don't just accept people's offers, but dictate exactly what you need without feeling bad, guilty or like a failure.'

WIDEN YOUR SUPPORT NETWORK

Not having family nearby to call on for help can really suck, especially when your friends start having evenings out or even weekends away with their partners. (Sleep? Peace and quiet? The audacity!) I've been there and felt green with envy. *But* you can absolutely widen your existing network to include more helpers who are not related to you.

Who in your life is close enough, location-wise as well as emotionally, to lend a hand? To come into your home to pick up the slack (and the dirty laundry off the floor)? To make a cup of tea and have a chat? Who knows your kitchen well enough to do the washing up *and* put it away? Could it be a neighbour, a work colleague, a friend?

I bet you anything that if you were to send out an email to colleagues, neighbours and friends who've had kids already and/or you feel close enough to, to ask for help in the postnatal period, you'd get many enthusiastic offers back. Don't be afraid to reach out. Don't let it get to the point where you're desperate for help because most likely you won't be able to think straight by that point. Pull people into your network early on and I promise, once you've taken that first step to ask for help, the sense of relief will be immense and the next time you reach out it will be much easier. It's so, so worth it because you really don't have to carry the weight of it all yourself.

UTILISE YOUR NEW BABY NETWORK

If you have done/are doing any kind of antenatal class, keep those folks close. They'll be going through everything you are at the same time, and it's invaluable. Even if you wouldn't normally have anything in common or hang out together, for the next year or so, these are your people.

They also become people you can walk with while your babies nap in the pram, people you can eat cake and cry with and who you can explore the world of baby groups with. They are the people who never tire of baby talk (unlike most child-free friends). They are the people who just 'get' it.

If you're not taking antenatal classes, I thoroughly recommend stalking groups of mums who seem nice and infiltrating their existing group. I successfully did this at a mum and baby exercise class after having baby number two and 100 per cent would do it again. I've also hit on mums in the playground who seem nice. Honestly, it's never been easier to start a conversation. Simply say, 'How did yours sleep last night?' and you're off.

I get that this seems like a very daunting prospect. Personally, I've struggled making friends my whole adult life, but the babies make it so much easier – there is so much common ground to chat about, so much sleep deprivation and freezing feet in the playground to bond over. And you don't have to make everyone your best friend. It's so helpful just to get to know a few people well enough to nod to from a distance or exchange a few words with at the baby swings. It's these little interactions that really carry you through it all. And if you strike gold and find a BFF, then that's an added bonus.

My most random act of 'network widening' was with a lady at the checkout in Boots who offered to babysit for me (I was always in there buying something baby-related and forever went on about how tired I was…). And I very nearly took her up on it. Help really might come from the most unlikely of places!

Once you're in the swing of motherhood a little more, you might even look at taking turns babysitting with other mums so you get a few hours or an evening free. To be honest, I was never brave enough to look after anyone else's babies (I was terrified enough of my own!), but this worked really well for friends of mine so I'm throwing it out there as an option.

IF YOU CAN STRETCH TO PAID HELP, DO IT

If you're able to, there's always the option of paying for help. Our wonderful cleaner saved my sanity when baby number two was born. She'd take my eldest around the house with her to 'help', so that I could just concentrate on baby.

A postnatal doula is also a wonderful thing – an extra pair of hands to show you the ropes, a shoulder to cry on, an ear to vent to, arms to hug you and simply another grown-up at home with you so you don't feel so isolated and overwhelmed. In hindsight, that's exactly what I needed in those early days and to this day I'm not sure why I didn't get one. I was possibly so consumed by the misconception that I could and should do it all myself, which is nonsense. Don't be like me! Since this is expert help, it does come with a price tag that won't be accessible for everyone, but it's still worth knowing that this service exists and maybe it can be recreated by some friends or family dropping in at regular intervals just to keep you company. They could create their own rota and everything – I sense a spreadsheet coming on!

A LITTLE WORD ABOUT GIFTS (AND HOW TO USE THEM IN THE CONTEXT OF ASKING FOR HELP!)

'When people ask what you need, could you ask for money for a postnatal doula, home help or a cleaner?'

Utilise your baby shower and people's desire to gift things for the baby to line up postnatal help. It's really tempting to ask for all the cute and practical baby things, but it might be more beneficial to receive vouchers or money towards home help, a postnatal doula, a cleaner or some meal deliveries. Anything that takes the pressure off you in the first few months is priceless. Even just another adult coming into your house for a conversation is magic. And if they're holding the baby while you're chatting, even better.

There's a Little Black Book section on page 144, which you can use to make a note of services in your area that might make helpful presents.

'I had twins and I wish I'd invested in proper help.'

Getting someone to do your cleaning, ironing or dog-walking for a while can free up some headspace. Meal delivery boxes and online supermarket orders might mean you can actually feed yourself well, while batch cooking things to pop in the freezer for a later date can be a lifesaver – even more so if you get friends to do it for you.

It's always worth keeping in mind that none of this needs to be forever, but it'll make life easier in the short term and that's what we're looking for.

CHEERLEADERS ARE HELPERS TOO

You might have people in your network of friends and family who can't physically help, but who could still support you by cheering you on and simply being there for you. Don't ever underestimate a phone call (or video call — one positive outcome from the coronavirus pandemic is that we're now all so used to these!) where you can vent and cry and laugh and be told that you are in fact doing an amazing job. Make sure to add plenty of cheerleaders to your list of people who you can lean on in the postpartum period.

TAKE THE PRESSURE OFF

Even if you're not getting actual hands-on help with the baby, simply taking the pressure off day-to-day tasks and chores can be a relief. Does it *really* matter that the house is dustier than it used to be? Or that the dishes don't get done? That you find clothes to wear from a heap of clean laundry, rather than out of a drawer? The expectations we have of ourselves in motherhood, be they self-imposed or spurred on by their portrayal in the media (socials as well as film, TV, magazines and books), are immense and unnecessary. Later in the book we explore how you can set priorities for this early parenting season in your life to work out exactly what matters to you, in your situation (see page 41).

Wouldn't it be nice if some kind of help was available on prescription? I heard from a friend the other day that a GP in Germany prescribed a mum with two kids under three two hours per day of home help. This makes so much sense to me, yet in the majority of the world you can get a prescription for mood-altering drugs before you can get physical support. There clearly needs to be more recognition in the medical and postnatal field about the struggles and juggles mothers go through with an emphasis on supporting both their mental and physical recovery, as opposed to a rushed six-week check with no further follow-up. Ideally, any support should be geared towards each individual and their unique circumstances rather than seeing all of us simply as 'a mum'. It would be complicated to set up, yes, but just imagine the money saved in the long run through having mothers properly supported, without developing long-term mental health or physical issues. Not forgetting the kids that get to grow up with much, much happier parents. We can but dream — and give feedback on unsatisfactory service, while also praising outstanding and helpful support!

SETTING BOUNDARIES AROUND HELP

Sometimes you might find that people are keen to help, but want to do things their own way, which might not gel with your style of parenting or general way of doing things. Other people might be OK with the baby crying for extended periods without giving it attention, think that an occasional bottle will be fine when you've been very clear that it's not or show total disregard for your carefully crafted nap and sleep routine.

These can be tricky situations to navigate and only a certain amount of experimentation will get you to a place where you know what you're OK with letting go and where you want to stand your ground. Conversations with your partner and closest family members will most likely occur again and again to make sure you're on the same wavelength.

If you want everything done absolutely 100 per cent your way, you might not ever let anyone else look after your child, including your partner. And that would be exhausting. So try to look at it this way: It's OK for kids to experience different kinds of caregiving. For example, it's OK that they learn that sitting still at the dinner table is important when Dad is present, but that Mum is OK with them grazing while playing. It's OK that grandparents give more treats and that nap time looks different at nursery or with the childminder.

But how do you go about actually putting boundaries in place without upsetting people? That's the million-dollar question!

Some of it will be trial and error — give people a chance, see how they do and then work out if the aftermath of whatever happened negates the actual help that was offered or if it was worth it. A little overtired bedtime grumble might be acceptable as a trade for a child-free afternoon, while two hours of crying because baby is overtired might not be. Each baby and situation is different, so I'd say give things a whirl and then adjust accordingly.

Presenting your team of helpers with information calmly is key. Telling them ahead of their next childcare stint that bedtime took three hours because baby was overtired might just persuade them to give that daytime nap a try. Some people will respond really well to being given directions and following instructions, even when they change; others might be resistant and get upset. Don't let things spiral into arguments, allow plenty of time for new information to land with your helper people and never make new boundary demands when you're feeling emotional in the moment. Cool off, sleep on it and plan your approach.

THE OPPOSITE OF HELPFUL

Just a little heads-up that some family members and friends might turn out to be less than helpful and that those who are keen to help might occasionally say or do the wrong thing. Instead of someone to lean on and who can pitch in, they might be expecting you to make them tea when they come to visit or even outlandish things like host Christmas with a tiny baby, simply because it's your turn. That's not OK and you're completely within your rights to say so.

Rather than taking it personally (which is easier said than done when tired and stressed out), calmly state what didn't work for you and, if they truly sport your team colours, they'll take note and do things better/differently next time. Any help offered has to truly work for you, otherwise it's just an extra headache for you to manage — and you don't need any more of those. Ask to have tea brought to you and skip a year (or three!) of Christmas hosting if you don't feel up to it. I personally don't anticipate hosting Christmas myself until my kids are grown-up!

If anyone is becoming more of a hindrance than a help, you can set boundaries around that and them: how often you see them, where you see them and whether they are allowed to look after your kid(s) by themselves. And it's A-OK to turn people away if they insist on turning up when it suits them, rather than checking when it suits you. You're the one who gets to say when you're ready for visitors. As far as I'm concerned, anyone with kids who are still in need of daytime naps gets to dictate when and where things happen. And new mums get to call *all* the shots.

A genius way of handling unwelcome surprise visitors is to pop a sign on the door that says something like 'Don't knock or ring — baby and Mum are sleeping'. And you don't even have to take that sign down when you/your baby have finished your nap!

'Views of people before children can change dramatically once they have had their own babies. Friends without babies (and older family members) can have very little understanding/memory of birth and the relentlessness of a newborn, so it's important to ask the right people for support. For example, my parents' view was that they'd already done this (having newborns) so now it was their turn to be waited on hand and foot...'

ACCEPT THE HELP

As a final parting thought on help — as well as asking for it in spades, please, please **accept it when it's offered.** 'I'm fine, thank you' tends to be our standard response to 'Is there anything I can do to help?' or its more passive cousin 'Let me know if there's anything I can do.' Pause for a second when someone asks you this to see what they could actually do to help and then answer honestly.

* Maybe someone could run an errand for you that would take you forever with baby in tow.

* Housework is always nice to have done by someone else — they may not know where all the laundry goes, but they can swing a hoover or a duster round.

* Could they push the pram round the park for baby's nap while you get some rest?

* Booking in a regular phone call or visit with someone could be a lovely way to break up the monotony of early motherhood.

* You don't have to like or even trust someone for them to drop off some brownies on your doorstep!

OVER TO YOU

It's time to get your thinking cap on and put pen to paper. Using the 'Who Can Support You?' planning space on page 21, make a list of who you could ask for help once baby arrives, so that you don't have to frantically try to think of people you can call on when you're in a sleep-deprived state. Even better — line them up now! Send an email, make a phone call... let them know they're on your list.

Remember to try to explore your wider network, not just close family and friends. Really spend some time thinking of possibilities and reach out to put things in place NOW. And don't forget that paid help counts, too, if that's within your budget.

'Make sure you have your family ready and waiting to support you in those first months. Someone to cook some meals for you, someone to hold baby while you have a nap off-duty, someone to clean the house for you, someone to give you a back rub, make you a cup of tea and tell you you are doing an amazing job.'

'Don't expect life to be blissfully happy just because you have your longed-for baby. It will be hard and exhausting. If you feel overwhelmed ASK FOR HELP. Don't keep on struggling on your own'.

THE GIST

Ask for help. Accept the help. Do not under any circumstances attempt to do it all on your own. It does indeed take a village.

CHARLOTTE TONKIN EDUN

DOULA

'Help' means more than you think. Having a new baby can make even the most emotionally hardy of us feel vulnerable. The sweeping changes of our bodies, however beautiful and wondrous, bring constant adjustment, minor and major. The dynamics of our relationships change too, often for the first time, and we become dependent on our partners in a way we may not have practised before; there is an acute shift from carefree independence to full-time, full-on responsibility that supersedes everything else. When your whole world is changing and you're trying to forge a new form of yourself, meeting the glossy expectations of new motherhood and domestic devotion can feel like a powerful way to demonstrate you are still 'You'. So asking for help can really feel like a failure. If you can't even do the washing up, remember to buy milk or have a shower, then what *are* you succeeding at?

Well, apart from the fact that motherhood is near-impossible to cope with without support, it's important to remember that accepting help has meaning that extends far beyond those hard weeks, days and hours of the fourth trimester. Offering and receiving support breathes new life into existing relationships. The help you seek and accept tells people around you what you need to thrive, not just survive. You're gently setting boundaries that feel comfortable to you, and helping new grandparents, friends and family understand how they fit into your new and improved family dynamic. Far from being a weakness, asking for help can be a powerful form of creation, as you extend your family and welcome 'your village'.

It doesn't matter what sort of help you want or need; remember that your acceptance of help means more than washing up, batch cooking or holding the baby while you satisfy your craving for a brisk walk, alone. Asking for and accepting help is more than material. It's that foundation of your future family.

WHO CAN SUPPORT YOU?

BUILD YOUR NETWORK

Create a list of people who might be suited to various types of support. Get their names down and get them lined up NOW. Ping them an email, give them a call, let them know they're on your list and what you'd like them to do. Some people might offer help off their own accord – add their names here, too, lovely people that they are.

EMOTIONAL SUPPORT

✳ Who would make an excellent cheerleader to call for a pep talk?

....
....
....

✳ Who can you vent or cry to without judgement?

....
....
....

✳ Who gives the best hugs?

....
....
....

✳ Who's already got kids and will give kind and useful advice and a listening ear?

....
....
....

✳ Who can pop round for some company?

....
....
....

PRACTICAL SUPPORT

What chores or errands could people help with? If you get them on board now, you could show them the ropes (and where things go in the kitchen cupboards).

What	Who
Food shop	
Washing up	
Hoovering	
Cleaning	
Cooking / food prep	
Taking baby for a walk	
Babysitting	
Other (anything specific to your circumstances)	

PROFESSIONAL (PAID) SUPPORT

Make a note of some contact details or, better still, get them booked in now:

* Postnatal doula:

  ....
  ....
  ....
  ....

* Home help:

  ....
  ....
  ....
  ....

* Cleaner:

  ....
  ....
  ....
  ....

* Favourite takeaways:

  ....
  ....
  ....
  ....

*   Other:

_____

_____

_____

_____

_____

_____

COMMUNITY SUPPORT

You can possibly leave this until after baby arrives, but it can be nice to know that you've already worked out a few places you and baby can hang out:

*   Mum and baby groups:

_____

_____

_____

_____

*   Favourite coffee shop (with plenty of space for prams):

_____

_____

_____

_____

✻ Anywhere locally with a crèche (gyms often have one):

_____

_____

_____

_____

_____

_____

✻ Other:

_____

_____

_____

_____

_____

_____

_____

_____

_____

CHAPTER 2

EXPLORING YOUR RELATIONSHIPS

FACT

Your relationship dynamic will change hugely.

BUT ALSO TRUE

You're a team! You've got this!

Adding a baby to any relationship dynamic changes it in ways that are impossible to foresee. When you throw a completely new lifestyle and sleep deprivation in a pot together and mix in a little bit of gender inequality and monotony, you'd be surprised how soon you'll have a big old resentment stew. You might find yourself timing how long your partner sat down for in any given day, begrudge them their train journey to work because they're able to read a book or feel incomparable rage towards their ability to sleep through anything. This may sound extreme and laughable, but is in fact common and totally normal. Big shifts happen in those first few months and your emotions certainly match them (see page 78).

If you're the one taking maternity leave, you're most likely the one who takes on the primary caregiver role. It's really, really easy to get stuck here and still find yourself doing the majority of everything months (even years!) down the line. But that doesn't have to be the case, which is exactly why the chapter on asking for and accepting help sits right at the start of this book! Reread it whenever necessary and get the helping hands that you need to stop yourself from feeling like the martyr who sacrifices everything for everyone and forever puts themselves last. There are also some tips in Chapter 4 for breaking out of this primary caregiver loop.

'So much falls to mums by default if they take maternity — do NOT do it! Make sure baby tasks are 50:50 from Day 1 and you don't end up doing them 'because you're better at it' (AKA have had lots of practice).'

SINGING FROM THE SAME PARENTING HYMN SHEET

It's worth keeping in mind that it's not just the parents who need to work out their new dynamic around the baby; your respective childhood and parenting experiences weigh in heavily here, too. The parenting you were modelled and experienced is either what you aspire to or want to move away from (although you won't even be aware of some subconscious behaviours and reactions). It's a great idea to give this a little bit of thought and discuss your findings with any other close caregivers in case there are blatantly opposing views. There's a prompt for this in the 'relationships' planning space on page 37 and our expert voice in this chapter delves more deeply into this topic, too (see page 34).

From personal experience, there wasn't much my husband and I disagreed on in the newborn stage – I think because we were simply both so overwhelmed and clueless! We had slight disagreements about how long or if at all to let the baby cry once she was a little older, but that was about it. (My mothering instincts won that argument easily!) A little later on I remember feeling almost offended when my husband wasn't interested in watching our daughter eat her first bites of solid food. How could he not be enthralled by her chomping on some broccoli? It's very comical to think about in retrospect, but at the time I was dead serious. Now that we're a little further along in our parenting journey, what irks me most is his overprotectiveness. He once stopped our two-year-old from running on a grassy field because she might fall over – it took a lot of effort for me not to counter that one.

Talking about the way we were both brought up (and in some instances still witnessing it on family visits) has helped with being able to accept or at least tolerate ways that we parent. I can see how my husband is trying to shake the overprotectiveness and how his behaviour is an improvement on what he experienced – he was only allowed to ride his bike in the garden until he was 16! My own Achilles heel is losing my temper and slipping into martyr mode, which is what I had modelled by my parents when I was little. Unfortunately, simply knowing why you act or react a certain way doesn't make it go away, but I'm working hard on improving all the time, which is all we can ever do.

'It can be so tough at points, but equally it's been so special to see what a great dad he is.'

'Apologise when you've messed up (to each other and to your kids) and aim to do better next time.'

TALK, TALK AND TALK SOME MORE

You'll get so bored but you've got to talk. Things that mildly bother you today might escalate into full-on rage in a few weeks if left unsaid. It takes a lot of effort to make this new dynamic work and not take every outburst or hiccup personally. Talk to each other (with the help of the handy planning sheet on page 37 to start, and then as and when things crop up) and make a list of people you can talk to, at length, about whatever you're going through – someone who gets it, who might be in a similar situation or who's simply good at listening. What's not ideal is to stew in your resentment – it turns so many ugly colours and spoils so many other areas of family life that have nothing to do with its origins. When it comes to resentment, out is definitely better than in!

BE A TEAM; DON'T BE THE COMPETITION

If at all possible, try not to count who sits down more, who gets more time away from the kid(s) or time for their hobbies and see yourselves as a team instead. You'll need that feeling of goodwill between each other to not constantly bicker, argue and feel resentful.

This is *much* easier said than done, especially once sleep deprivation kicks in and every little thing that only slightly bothered you before is now amplified by 100, but try to remind yourself every now and again that you love this person, that they love you and that you each actually want the best for each other. This, of course, requires that the other person/people are on the same page about all of this – hence the emphasis on talking about e-v-e-r-y-t-h-i-n-g.

'Remember that you love your partner, because it may feel like you hate them in those early weeks. Don't forget that it's confusing and daunting for them too and they deserve some support. They're not the enemy.'

A rule of thumb that I've heard time and time again is this: make no big decisions in the first year after having a kid. It takes that long for the dust to settle enough to think somewhat clearly again. If you need to do things like move house or switch jobs, it's doable of course, but it's definitely not easy. Plan for the fact that things will take longer and be more emotionally charged. Then, if they're not – hurrah!

WHO DOES WHAT WHEN?

It's beyond helpful to establish a partner's role in the daily routine with a newborn. If feeds can be shared, that's a fantastic starting point and potentially means some extra sleep for you every now and again. If you're breastfeeding and that's not a possibility, look at what other tasks in the household can be divvied up differently. Can your partner do the cooking? Can they do the cleaning? Or even both? Can your partner get up and bring baby to you to feed so you don't have to get out of bed? Can they take over some life logistics, like booking dentist and doctor appointments for a while? Anything to free up some headspace and take stuff off your mental plate.

As baby gets older, the things a partner, family or friend can do instead of you increase exponentially: bath times, meal times, walks, trips to the playground. You're not stuck in newborn land forever! Line those helpers up (see Chapter 1).

Little gestures in the early weeks and months – when date nights, trips away or simply having time for just the two of you are limited – mean A LOT. Takeaway food brought home, remembering to pick up dirty laundry off the floor, a squeeze and a kiss even though you've not showered for days, silly dances, bad jokes... they all help you feel connected.

My husband used to set up a 'feeding station' for me before he left for work in the morning. He'd make sure there were snacks, tissues, the remote control and a big bottle of water next to the sofa where I sat feeding the baby. He felt helpful, I felt looked after, and it really took the edge off the aforementioned resentment about him getting to sit on a train for an hour!

If you're caring for baby alone, maybe friends and family could drop off care packages to keep you supplied with treats and essentials.

'The exhaustion and resentment of the other person (they get to bugger off to work versus you getting to spend time with the child) can get pretty intense if you don't talk about it.'

'Lean on your partner. Help them help you and tell them how because, if you don't, they won't know! I fell into blaming my partner for not helping when they didn't know any better than me what on earth we were meant to be doing!'

THE HIGHS, THE LOWS AND THE EMOTIONAL OUTBURSTS

The emotional rollercoaster of the first few months is no joke. The hormones of the early weeks aside, many women report an ability to erupt with absolute fury at the tiniest thing, unlike anything they've known before. It can be pretty scary for everyone involved. I used to ask my husband for a hug when I had outbursts like that, which took him a really long time to wrap his head around. All he could see was someone really, really red-hot angry with him. I, on the other hand, was scared of the intensity of my reactions and needed some physical contact to help calm and soothe me. This is where talking comes in handy again. I spy a theme here!

To prepare for this emotional upheaval in a small way, use the planning space on page 37 to think about how you and your partner and/or other adults around you deal with stress. Do they get angry or emotional? Do you withdraw? Have open and honest chats about how to best support each other when the going gets tough. Maybe you haven't had conversations like that before, but it'll be harder to do when you're sleep-deprived and grumpy already.

As an example, when my husband feels down, he needs me to carry on as normal and almost jolly him along, whereas I need hugs and verbal reassurance. While what we each need feels alien to ourselves, we know that it helps the other person, so we do it. (OK, so maybe it's not quite as easy as that — there are still lots of reminders necessary, but we're not starting from scratch each time.)

Your partner is not a mind reader and neither are you. As nice as it would be for someone to simply guess what you need and give you exactly that, it's not very likely to happen. On the other hand, if you ask for what you need, you're so much more likely to get exactly that.

While navigating this early part of motherhood alongside those closest to you, it's worth keeping in mind that, for the first couple of weeks, your hormones will be all over the place, which can contribute to mood swings and floodgates of tears opening without any warning. This treat of an emotional rollercoaster is labelled the 'baby blues' and affects pretty much everyone. Your body and brain are trying to regain some equilibrium after growing and birthing a little person, which is a bumpy process to start. Having said that, if you find that your mood remains low for any length of time, you don't find enjoyment in things you normally like or are experiencing thoughts of harming yourself or your baby, these can be signs of postnatal depression (PND) and it's really important to seek extra support. The line between baby blues and PND is very blurry and, you guessed it, talking it out will be the most helpful thing to distinguish what's going on for you. See Chapter 6 (page 77) for more on PND and how to get support.

THE GIST

Becoming parents is a big shift in any relationship. Keep talking about how you're experiencing it and share all household- and kid-related chores as equally as possible from the start.

DR JENNY TURNER

CLINICAL PSYCHOLOGIST

Have you ever really explored the things you loved about how your parents raised you? Or explored the things you hated about the way you were parented?

Most of us don't think too deeply about this before we have kids, but these questions are more important than you might realise... Because how we were parented ourselves, and how we feel about that, both impact enormously on how we will parent our own children — particularly in 'autopilot' moments or in those moments when we are stressed or emotionally triggered.

The more conscious we can become of how our childhood experiences impact on our parenting, the more we can switch off that autopilot, which means we can more often be the type of parent we *want* to be, rather than the type of parent we were *unconsciously conditioned* to be.

We can really give ourselves a head start on our parenting journey if we begin to consciously explore our own experiences of childhood. If you're not sure where to begin, here are some starter questions to ask yourself:

*   Were your parents very strict at home when you were a child? Or were you free to explore or make a mess/be loud/make mistakes, etc.? Was one of your parents stricter than the other? If so, which one?

*   Were you always cuddled to sleep? Or were you left to cry it out before falling asleep?

* Did you learn early how to feed yourself, and were you allowed to revel in the mess that comes along with that? Or were you spoon-fed and cleaned up by your parent as you ate?

* Were you the 'good girl/boy' or the 'rebel'? Did you follow orders as a child or did you push against authority?

* Were you encouraged to cry and share your feelings as a child? Or when you were upset were you told: 'It's not that bad', 'Be strong', 'Stop crying' or 'Pull yourself together'? Or, conversely, were you told to 'Calm down' when you were excited or happy?

* Did you always have two parents, who were always present? Or did one parent work very long hours? Or did one parent leave the family home to live elsewhere at some point?

This list is not exhaustive, of course, and asking yourself these questions may well lead to more questions, and more exploring. However, once you become more consciously clear about your own experiences, you can then ask yourself: 'In what ways do I want to parent my child in the same ways that I was parented?' And, conversely, 'In what ways do I want to parent differently?'

As you embark upon this exploration, it's important to remember that your partner has also had their own experience of parenting, and it will be different to yours, even if the experiences look similar on the surface.

It's generally accepted that it's a good idea for parents to be on the 'same page' when parenting, yet it's rarely acknowledged that we are always starting that journey from very different pages. It actually takes a lot of conscious effort and repeated, respectful communication to forge that 'same-page parenting'.

I therefore recommend that each parent do this exercise individually, and then I encourage you to talk to each other about your respective experiences. And do also keep in mind that these are often not easy exercises to complete, nor are they easy conversations to have. Both may bring up some challenging emotions and feelings — it takes courage to confront our past, and to talk to others about it. For those who have the resources to access therapy, working through these conversations with a therapist can be invaluable.

However you dive into these explorations and conversations, take it slowly, be kind to yourself and each other, and acknowledge the awkwardness and vulnerability that inevitably comes up in these discussions. And always take a break when you need one.

It is also important to remember that the type of parent you will sometimes *find yourself being*, particularly in high-stress moments, is inevitably going to be very different to the type of parent you *want to be* — no matter how much self-exploration you've done or how much therapy you've had. So when you do sometimes react unconsciously and emotionally, my advice is again to show yourself some self-compassion and remind yourself of this: There is nothing wrong with any of us when we do this. This is us simply being human.

Despite how shameful or guilt-ridden we all inevitably feel in those moments, it is truly not those moments that matter the most in the long run — it's what we do next, after those moments... If we can notice that it happened and then be compassionate to ourselves, while gently acknowledging the roots of these moments in our own childhood, and reminding ourselves that there is nothing wrong with us, then we are doing incredible things for our mental health as parents.

And finally, if we can also remember to say to our child: 'I'm sorry I reacted like that, that was not your fault, there is nothing wrong with you', then we will also be doing incredible things for our child's mental health in the long run.

RELATIONSHIPS

Any time is a good time for a relationship chat! Below are some topics to chat about before or after the baby is born. Note down answers for each of you and refer back to them later on. Do add your own questions that seem relevant to your situation.

✳ What are your expectations of life with a small baby?

....

....

....

....

....

✳ What sacrifices do you see yourself making?

....

....

....

....

....

....

* What household chores could be divided differently?

....

....

....

....

* How do you cope with sleep deprivation?

....

....

....

....

* How do you both deal with stress?

— Do you get angry/defensive/sad/depressed/withdraw/ compensate with humour?

....

....

....

....

* What are your stress triggers?

....

....

....

....

*   What's your history of mental health issues?

*   When might you need to ask for further support?

*   How do you like to be comforted when you're:

    —   sad:

    —   upset:

— stressed:

....

....

....

— anxious:

....

....

....

✶ What did/didn't you like about the way you were parented/raised?

....

....

....

....

....

✶ Is there anything about parenting that you feel super strongly about (that you either never, ever want to do or absolutely have to)?

....

....

....

....

....

....

CHAPTER 3

WORKING OUT YOUR PRIORITIES

(AKA THERE'S ONLY SO MUCH
YOU CAN DO, AKA LOWER
THE BAR ON EVERYTHING)

You won't have as much time for yourself as you do now.

If you work out what's really important to you, finding your feet in motherhood will be a lot easier.

Before having a baby, it's really hard to fathom exactly how much of your time they'll take up. Let me tell you now — it's a lot. In fact, it's utterly astounding that we manage to do anything besides caring for the baby. Looking back, I cannot understand how I used to fill my time before having kids. It just makes no sense. I certainly didn't spend it cleaning because my house was just as messy... what on earth did I do with myself?!

The thing is, babies really do need you for everything — they depend on you for food, comfort and safety (and also transportation for a large chunk of their first few years). By just meeting those needs (imperfectly a lot of the time, which is fine!), you're rocking a full-time job; one that's badly paid at that and that everyone has an opinion on which they're desperate to share with you — urgh.

As much as you can, just focus on that new full-time job for a bit. You're getting to know your baby, you're discovering the new motherhood version of yourself and you're working out new relationship dynamics and practically reinventing your life. That takes time. Be patient with yourself and those around you (baby, too).

It's totally possible and very normal to fill a whole day with feeding, nappy changes, facilitating naps and generally working out what on earth you're doing. I remember messaging my husband around eight weeks into life with a newborn, ecstatic because I'd managed to take out the bins (on the right day no less!). It felt like such an accomplishment! To his credit, he appropriately celebrated with me.

A DAY IN THE LIFE OF/WITH A NEWBORN

When I was pregnant, I was desperate to know what life with a baby would actually look like. As I mentioned in the Introduction, I actually asked my antenatal teacher what we'd do once we brought the baby home and annoyingly didn't get an answer. So I've created a little melange of things that are likely to happen during the course of a day with your newborn or across the first few months. I've purposely not created a timeline for a 'typical' day because there is no such thing. Not only is every baby different, but every day with your baby will be different, too. There is a glimmer of hope for routine on the horizon at some point in the future though, so sit tight.

* Changing nappies. So, so many times. Including in the middle of the night (this doesn't last forever – hang on in there!).

* Changing baby's clothes because of poo leakage. Sometimes this also means a change for you.

* Changing you and/or baby, this time because of puke (theirs, not yours hopefully).

* A lot of laundry (unsurprisingly, given the previous two points).

* Baby naps on you x 4/5. If you're lucky, you get to sit down. If not, it's time for constant movement (sling, pram, car).

* Watching them sleep and marvel at their perfect little nose and fingers and eyelashes and cheeks.

* Feeding.

* Feeding again; every two hours when they're newborn. And that's from the start of the last feed, not the end. It comes round again exhaustingly quickly.

* Burping baby – cycling through about five different positions to make sure it's been effective.

* Cleaning baby bottles.

* Trying to get out of the door to 'pop' to the shop. Pack bag with everything you might need. Baby poops as you leave so back in you go to change another nappy.

Less important side note: Leaving the house with a baby for the first time is quite something. I felt nervous, shaky, couldn't get the pram to work, then baby started crying and I got more and more flustered. Turns out, everyone feels the same on their first trip out! You'll get used to all the things you'll need to schlepp around with you (and you'll still find muslin cloths, baby wipes, rogue plasters and snack packets in your bag years later), but quickly nipping out somewhere is not so easy anymore.

General rule of walks with a baby: as long as the pram is moving, baby is happy/asleep (they *love* movement), all is good.

* Working out how the car seat fits on the pram/in the car, how the rain cover is meant to stretch over the entire thing, what pocket in the change bag works best for what, etc.

* Staring into space (or your chosen box set) while baby stretches out on the floor for a bit.

* Googling various baby-related things (cluster feeding, cradle cap, baby acne, growth spurts, wonder weeks, electronic 'shush them to sleep' devices, nipple shields, sleep-inducing lotions and potions, pram gloves, 15 different types of teats for bottles that might never be taken, muslins – you always need more muslins).

* Spending too much time and money online (see previous point).

* Chatting to other mums on FB groups, apps and baby forums (are they still a thing?).

* Eating carbs for energy and perfecting one-handed eating of pretty much anything.

* Overthinking absolutely everything while going through the above list. Worrying about the amount of milk baby has had and the consistency and colour of their bowel movements.

* Oversharing with partners and family – optional, but highly likely.

Yes, this can certainly feel as exhausting and repetitive as it looks. Which is why asking for help and creating a support network is so important. Having someone to tag team with every now and again to alleviate the monotony is literal magic. And it's also the reason for getting super clear on what's important for you to hang on to from your life before baby. There's only a limited amount of time to fit stuff for yourself into, so being super selective about what makes the cut is really key. Remember that you can always shift your priorities as and when things change – nothing is set in stone.

So, if pretty much all of your time is taken up by childcare, how on earth do you make time for anything else? Below are some tips to get you started, and we'll also loop back to this in Chapter 4 (see page 53).

CUT YOURSELF SOME SLACK

As I've mentioned already, the most important and kindest thing you could possibly do is cut yourself lots of slack and give yourself time to adjust to motherhood without judgement, comparison or rush. There are some tips to help with this in Chapters 10 and 11 on managing mum guilt and avoiding comparison where I explore the concept of good-enough parenting/mothering. Bye bye perfection, hello good enough!

WHAT'S IMPORTANT ENOUGH TO MAKE THE CUT?

Thinking about the kinds of things you'd like to carry over from your 'old' life and how you can adapt them to fit into your new lifestyle can be really useful.

If you're still pregnant when you're reading this, it's an excellent idea to spend some time thinking about what you, as your pre-mum self, enjoy doing. What makes you tick, what makes you happy, what makes you YOU? It's not that you won't have *any* time to yourself once you're a mum, it's just going to be a lot more limited, so getting clear now on what you'd like to still make time and space for will be really helpful. This doesn't have to be anything big. Simply think of things that make you feel good: music, hobbies, time alone, work, sleeping, time with friends, etc. What makes you feel charged up and refreshed; what makes you feel rested and recovered? You'll be so glad you have this to refer to later on, I promise. With the best will in the world, it's incredibly difficult not to get completely lost in newborn land, and anything you note down now will be priceless to point you in the right direction later on.

If you've already had your baby, don't fret. Any time is a good time to take a few minutes to work out what's really important to you. You can either transport yourself back into your pre-pregnancy shoes or look at things from your current perspective – or a bit of both. Whenever you're ready, head to the 'Setting Your Priorities' planning space on page 49 to jot down some non-negotiables for yourself: What is it that you need every day/week/month to feel like you and to feel your best? And what can you let go of or at least do less of?

While working through this, keep in mind that the priorities you set won't have to be like this forever. Just because cleaning and playing hockey take a backseat for now, doesn't mean it'll always be that way. Things shift and change *all* the time, and revisiting your priority notes every now and again will be useful. Regularly revisit your list and ask yourself, 'Is that still true for me now?' – three, six, twelve months into motherhood (and beyond).

When we had our first baby, I ended up having a conversation with my husband about how neat we needed the house to be to feel happy. It turns out his tolerance level for mess was way higher than mine, hence why he didn't pick up any slack — because, to him, there wasn't any. So I decided that, until further notice, I wouldn't worry about mess too much or making our house look like a show home. Now, nine years on and another kid later, a hidden nook of headspace seems to have unlocked — I've purchased new storage solutions, bought plants and painted a feature wall! While it's not always easy to stick to the priorities you've set for yourself (sometimes the clutter really gets to me and I wish we had a minimalist house with no toys in it or at least a toy room to shut the door on), if you're clear about them, you can remind yourself why you've set them in this way and that it's only temporary.

WHAT GETS CUT?

To make room for the things you *do* want to do, you'll need to find things that you're OK to let go of, lower your standards on or delegate. Some things could be done less frequently or outsourced (ironing!) and if exercising seeing friends/crocheting/playing the harp has to fit in somewhere somehow, maybe there need to be frozen dinners a few nights a week to make that happen. Could you get away with hoovering less often or not shaving your legs for this particular season in life? Take the pressure off in as many areas of life as possible. If you think you're done cutting, cut some more. If you think you've asked for enough helping hands, ask for more.

EXPECTATIONS VERSUS REALITY

The discrepancy between your expectations of motherhood and the reality you then find yourself living in can really complicate setting priorities. If you've pictured sun-drenched, tidy spaces in which you blissfully hang out with a baby who sleeps beautifully and the reality is a clutter of baby paraphernalia in a dim room that smells faintly of baby vomit, that contrast is likely to make you a little unhappy.

I'd always pictured myself as an active mum who'd go to the gym a lot and run with baby in the pram. Both things did happen, just *a lot* less frequently than I'd anticipated and I was a hell of lot more tired doing them!

Of course, there's no way to imagine all the possible realities of what motherhood might look like for you and it's fine to daydream and fantasise – that can be so much fun! Just try not to get too emotionally attached to a particular idea or image. Keep your mind – and your options – open!

Coming to terms with your reality of motherhood can take a while. It's important you take some time to get your bearings and work out whether your priorities and expectations need shifting somewhat. Talking this through with friends and people close to you will help, once again, to get clarity here. Sometimes you don't realise how silly a belief that you hold is until you speak it out loud. I had somehow convinced myself that hoovering downstairs once a day was the benchmark of me coping with motherhood and housework. When I mentioned this to my husband one day, he asked if he could do it instead. I'm not joking when I say that it felt like 30 per cent of tension left my body! When so much around us feels out of our control, we can latch on to the silliest things to make us feel like we still have a sense of agency.

> *'Lower your expectations of what a clean house/put-together person looks like. A lot. And then some more.'*

'Don't do anything in those first few weeks! Literally stay in bed or on the sofa! Everything else can wait.'

THE GIST

Your priorities will shift in motherhood and it's a good idea to make a note of what makes the cut to the other side. Lower the bar on everything else. A lot.

'I'm learning not to put too much expectation for perfection on to myself and to be kinder. It's the biggest transition and there are lots of ups and downs along the way!'

'Expectations of winning at life will change and that's absolutely normal. It's OK to wear clothes with elasticated waistbands for a while.'

SETTING YOUR PRIORITIES

* What makes you feel happy, joyful and fulfilled? Everything and anything counts. You can always come back and add things later as you think of them.

* How can you still do all or some of the above after baby arrives?

* How can you adapt and simplify it and/or who can help facilitate the time needed?

CREATING NON-NEGOTIABLES

✱ What *has* to happen every day/week/month to keep you happy and well? Be specific if at all possible, assigning times and circumstances: 'I'll shower at 7am every morning before my partner goes to work' or 'every second Saturday I'll have two hours to do as I please'.

Daily:
(Shower, eight glasses of water and at least one vegetable...)

....

....

....

....

Weekly:
(Exercise, alone time...)

....

....

....

....

Monthly:
(Lunch with friends, half a day to myself...)

....

....

....

....

....

INSTRUCTIONS FOR LOWERING THE BAR

✳ What can you do less well?
  (Cooking (oven food for the win!), cleaning...)

_____

_____

_____

_____

_____

_____

_____

_____

✳ What can you do less often?
  (Replying to emails, giving in to demands from the in-laws...)

_____

_____

_____

_____

_____

_____

_____

_____

*   What can you stop doing altogether?
(Dusting, ironing…)

_____

_____

_____

_____

_____

_____

_____

*   What can you delegate or outsource?
(Hiring a cleaner, shifting a chore on to someone else's plate…)

_____

_____

_____

_____

_____

_____

_____

_____

_____

BALANCING YOUR OLD LIFE WITH MUM LIFE

Your life will change more than you can currently comprehend.

You *will* find your groove and ways to do things your own way.

You'll most likely miss your 'old life' once your baby arrives, and that's totally OK. We all have that one friend who manages to take a tiny baby skiing or still shares pictures of lengthy workouts and date nights on social media, but even for that person certain things will have changed – we just can't see that in their snapshots (I cover comparison in Chapter 11, so make sure you read that, too, if that tends to trip you up). People like that are exceptions, not the rule.

As much as you might be willing things to go back to 'normal', that's not going to happen any time soon and baby won't simply tag along to things that you used to do. It's a tough adjustment to make, and it will take some time, both physically and mentally. Berating yourself for not adjusting 'better' or faster won't make it happen any quicker, it'll just make it a lot more unpleasant. Being kind and gentle with yourself is by far the better approach – you want to be on your own side and have your own back.

It's OK to grieve for your old life. In my experience and opinion, people who say they can't remember their life before kids are lying. Sure, you might not miss or remember aspects of it, but the general 'no responsibilities, free time and extra money' vibe of it is pretty hard to forget.

I still grieve whole Sundays on the sofa watching films, while at the same time feeling beyond grateful that I get to call two amazing little girls my daughters. It's totally possible and absolutely OK to miss something, while also being thankful for something else. You're not 'doing motherhood wrong' because you wish you could eat lunch in peace and have a lie-in until 10am.

It's also OK if motherhood alone doesn't make you feel fulfilled. It's normal and important to still want to do things for yourself or go back to work. You're allowed to still be your own person besides 'Mummy'. So many women, including me, lose themselves in motherhood, totally sacrificing themselves for their kids and then not being able to recognise themselves when they come up for air a few years later. It's then really, really tricky to make a start on getting back to yourself and can also mean that you end up feeling resentful towards other people in your life who have been able to retain the majority of their 'old' life. I used to time how long my husband would go running for (including his leisurely shower once he got back) and seethe at the injustice that my allocated 'exercise slot' fell short of his by almost an hour. Small inequalities add up really quickly and, before you know it, you begrudge someone having a rest because they 'didn't need to run that far'. Not my proudest wife moment/marriage phase...

HOW TO BYPASS THE RESENTMENT

The only way to swerve this level of resentment and mummy martyrdom is to ask for help and support (see Chapter 1 for the 'how to') and retain elements of your old life that were meaningful to you, in whatever way they now fit into your new life. Long runs might become walks for a bit, before they become runs again. Your yoga practice might be bite-sized with some company on the mat. Audio books could make an appearance instead of flipping actual pages. Having a ponder about these kinds of adjustments can be super helpful in preparation for becoming a mum and ease the sense of not having anything for yourself anymore in those first few months.

BECOMING A MUM IS A BIG DEAL

Becoming a mum is such a huge transition; it even has its own name – 'matrescence'. No, I didn't know that either. Not for the first seven years of motherhood. Had I known, a lot of things would have made a lot more sense!

While 'adolescence' describes the transition from late childhood to early adulthood, matrescence is the physical, emotional, hormonal and social transition to becoming a mother. And while the hormonal and physical changes of the teenage years are well known and well-documented, that's not the case with the transition into motherhood. Yet the process of matrescence brings with it an equal amount of change and transformation, and some experts believe it can take up to ten years to fully transition through it (eek!). I will only go into a little bit of detail here, but I'll link to some resources (see page 142) that you can use as a jumping off point if you'd like to delve a little deeper. It really is fascinating.

My second kid was a couple of years old when I stumbled across this term. The fact that the adjustment period of becoming a mother has a name was mind-blowing to me. Simply seeing someone acknowledge that it takes adjusting to was huge. Alexandra Sacks, whose TED Talk on the subject is amazing and who is also a reproductive psychiatrist, states that she's witnessed women visibly relax when they are told that it is normal to find motherhood difficult. The weight lifted by having this spoken out loud is immense. Had someone told me that it was normal to find bits of motherhood incredibly difficult, it would have definitely taken the edge off. The relief! Simply knowing that something isn't meant to be plain sailing and that what we're going through is normal takes the pressure off enormously.

In fact, I remember the moment the motherhood struggle got normalised for me. I was sitting in a café with my one-and-a-half-year-old in the high chair next to me. A mum, who had a younger baby and toddler, joined us and casually said, 'Only a few months to go until this becomes fun – I'm really not a fan of the baby stage.' I think my mouth might have dropped open. It's OK to feel that? It's OK to *say* that? Hallelujah! 'Not a fan of the baby stage' – that's me. I've joked (but am actually deadly serious) that when there are grandkids on the scene, they're not staying overnight until they can talk. Some people love the baby stage, but it terrifies me.

SHIFTING PERSPECTIVES AND MAKING FRIENDS WITH CHANGE

As well as early motherhood being an adjustment period to navigate with patience and kindness towards yourself (and a made-up song and silly dance to match if you're in my house), it also puts a totally different lens on your outlook on life. Different things become important. Maybe the long commute is no longer worth it, maybe the job you're on maternity leave from seems less appealing (or maybe you can't wait to get back, which is also fine!). What hobbies are going to make the cut to fit into your new life? What friendships will make it and what other mums share equal values to you? Depending on the answers to those questions, your friendship circle might change significantly.

You might well carry on enjoying nights out with your childless friends, or you might find that you don't have so much in common anymore. Either outcome is fine. Friendships changing, evolving or dissolving is fine. And new friendships might be different, too. People you meet because your babies are a similar age have a lot in common with you right now, which is super comforting and important, but they may not be the kind of people you would have been friends with before. As your kids get older, it's fine if you drift apart again – or you might find you've made friends for life. Again, it's all OK. There's no right or wrong way to make/keep friends in motherhood. And you might even find that holy grail of friendships – the ones who don't mind if you're not in touch for ages but you effortlessly pick up right where you left off whenever you chat or meet up.

IT'S ONLY A PHASE (RINSE AND REPEAT OVER AND OVER)

While breaking in your motherhood hat, you might go through phases of loving being a mum, contrasted with phases of wanting to get as far away from your family as possible and staying there... sometimes in the space of a couple of minutes. It can be mind-bogglingly contradictory, but fear not, there's a term for this, too, and it's also completely normal. It's called 'maternal ambivalence' and describes the push and pull of motherhood, wanting to be close to your children but equally craving your own space and trying to find a balance between both when in actual fact that's almost impossible, as life shifts and changes so much when kids are young. If you can find a way to be OK with feeling both of these things at once, then you're on to a winner. Most of the time, the experience of motherhood is neither good *nor* bad, it's *both* good *and* bad. Learning to tolerate this ambivalence brings with it a lot of peace and less struggle and resistance.

Whenever you find yourself caught in a motherhood whiplash of emotions ('I love cuddles' versus 'Get off me and give me some space, I can't do another second of this' versus 'Oh, look at them sleeping! This is the best!'), rather than beating yourself up about not enjoying all of motherhood, try acknowledging the bits that are hard along with the things that are wonderful. By not ignoring or shoving down the more difficult moments and emotions, we let them come up for air and sit alongside the lovely stuff. There's space for both. This takes practice (and reminding yourself to do it!), but it is so worth working on. A simple statement of 'I'm finding this hard' can often be enough to lighten the load significantly. Just naming what's going on for you frees up valuable headspace and shoos some tension out of the shoulders.

There *absolutely* are ways to fit what you need into your mothering days, as long as you can accept that it won't look like it did pre-baby.

'Your life will never be the same again. People who tell you it won't change you are mistaken, have never done it, did it so long ago they've forgotten they changed or are lying. You will mourn the old you and your old life and you should, too, because your life was cool and you were already happy, right?! The good news is that although it's different, the new life has happiness too... it's just maybe not immediately obvious!'

'If you don't suddenly love the new and massive changes in your life, that's OK and lots of other new mums feel the same way.'

'I struggled with my sense of self. Who am I as a mum? Having been a professional and party person, the sleepless nights and incompatibility of exclusively breastfeeding sucked the life out of the old me, and left me feeling all 'mum'. Something I'm still working to rectify now.'

KEEP YOURSELF ENTERTAINED

While your baby is very tiny and needs to feed a lot, you'll be on your own at home for large chunks at a time and it's a good idea to create a list of things that might entertain you and break up the monotony and repetition of infant care every day. I made my way through all seasons of *True Blood* and *Buffy* when my first was tiny – maybe somehow connected to the feeling of being sucked dry?! I've never made that connection until now, how funny! The second time round I was obsessed with *Once Upon a Time* and *Orphan Black*. Binge, binge, binge.

You might have plans of learning a language, picking up a new hobby or reading lots. And while you might well do some of that, it's also very possible that you won't. Both sleep deprivation and the brain fog that descends in new motherhood (to make sure you're focusing all your attention on keeping your offspring alive – more on that later) are no joke and the easier entertainment is digested, the better.

Those early days are like a weird motherhood vortex – you've never been busier, yet you're getting nothing done. And a lot of what you do do (doo-doo – get it? Get used to poo jokes now, they'll be all the rage in a couple of years) can feel a little on the relentless and boring side of things: changing nappies, making food/bottles, sitting down to feed, settling baby down for naps — it all comes round again, day after day after day.

Here are some ways that helped me make the monotone less monochrome:

* Put on your favourite music — an instant pick-me-up.

* Sing or hum: during nappy changes, when baby cries, when you want to cry (or scream), it works a bloody charm. Make songs up or put them on and sing along — sing out. Baby loves it, and you'll feel better. Everybody wins. Extra bonus — humming actually helps to calm your nervous system!

* Get outside: it doesn't matter if it's just round the block, nature somehow brings instant perspective. It's awesome.

* Talk to another grown-up: even a supermarket checkout person counts at a pinch.

* To mimic adult company, pop on podcasts or talk radio (take advantage of the time before your baby can talk all over it or when you have to screen for swear words!).

* Make sure you're comfortable at all times. This is not the time for restrictive clothing, slipping bra straps or outfits without pockets.

* Read books with super short chapters that are easy to dip in and out of. Even reading just one page can be enough to realise you can think of things outside of baby care.

* Always have some of your favourite food in, whether that's chocolate or sushi. You need to treat yourself.

* Have some WhatsApp groups going with friends — some who have babies and some who don't. Maybe one could be purely for sharing silly memes.

* Curate your social media feed. If you're going to be scrolling, make sure it's all stuff that either makes you feel good or makes you laugh. There's more on this in Chapter 11.

> *'Having a child can ironically be the loneliest time of your life when you are never alone.'*

GIVE YOURSELF TIME TO RECOVER

The idea of 'bouncing back' after birth is such a myth and depends on the kind of pregnancy and birth you had, your age and how much you're able to rest after birth (i.e. how much help you're getting postnatally). Remember that the celebs/influencer types who make it appear that 'snapping back' is possible, tend to have an army of help around that makes sure they're fed, watered, rested and exercised optimally. We're generally making do with finger food and power naps. There's a big difference!

I remember feeling so frustrated (almost betrayed) at the unfairness of needing to recover from birth (stitches from an episiotomy) while being so tired and overwhelmed. I'd never needed to heal so much, yet I couldn't sleep or rest like I would have done before. I couldn't see how I'd ever heal and, while I did, of course, there are things I could have done to help myself, even without family around. A doula is definitely one of those things that, in hindsight, I should have booked in (see page 24).

One doula I know gets the mum-to-be and all close relatives to sign a contract that states no visitors for the first week and as much bed rest for the new mother as possible (only getting up to go to the toilet or to have a shower). She physically evicts anyone who goes against the contract to guarantee as stress-free a first week as possible.

And there are plenty of cultures where two weeks of staying in bed is common practice for new mums. Relatives take care of everything else, including making nourishing food for the mother. All she has to do is rest, feed and bond with baby. While that's not possible for most of us, who are often far away from our extended family, you can, and should, adopt elements of this recovery model – for example, not allowing visitors until you're ready, and on your terms (read: telling them to make their own damn cup of tea and why not do the washing up while they're at it). And mostly know that it's OK, and vital, to rest. Motherhood is a marathon, not a sprint. Keep reminding yourself of that (I still do!).

It might be a good idea to start following some body-positive social media accounts now, especially those that focus on realistic postnatal recovery or those that share a variety of postnatal bodies. One massive bonus of our social media feeds is that we can curate them to see only the things that we want to see. So it's time to unfollow those accounts that make you feel less than or not enough or that make you feel itchy with comparison. There's no need for that.

GETTING MOVING AGAIN

If you're keen to get back to exercise, it's super important that you do so safely and in a way that supports your recovery.

Your first port of call will be your six-week check with your GP. They are meant to clear you for exercise, which unfortunately means wildly different things to different doctors. At the very least, they should check in on your mental health (please be as honest as you can about that) and examine you for abdominal separation. Neither time did my GP do either of those things; both times I made them. Postnatal follow-up care can be lacking and if we all demand better, maybe it'll get better!

If you've had a C-section or any sort of stitches following birth, these should most certainly be checked and the type of exercise you're planning on doing should be taken into account. Walking is different to running, which is different to yoga, which is different to lifting weights. If your GP is unsure, err on the side of caution, take your time, listen to your body and, if you can, get advice and a once-over from a women's health physio or similar.

In an ideal world, in my opinion, every new mum should work with a qualified postnatal personal trainer, or someone at their gym who's hot on that sort of stuff, to make sure the focus is on exercises that meet each mum where they're at, without putting them or their recovery in danger. All exercise at this stage should a) make you feel good and b) support normal function to return across all muscle groups. Your body worked around a bump for months, it takes some tweaking and readjusting to get used to being on your own again.

THE GIST

Becoming a mother is a huge adjustment. Give your body and mind time to catch up with itself and it's OK to not 'enjoy every minute' of motherhood. It feels hard because it is hard.

EMMA JEFFERY

POSTNATAL PERSONAL TRAINER

Your body will naturally adapt during pregnancy to accommodate your growing baby. From changes in posture to weakening muscles, abdominal separation and pelvic pressures, all of this is part of the process. Your birth experience can also potentially put added and varying strains on your body and, once your baby has been born, these demands do not stop with soothing, cuddling, feeding, lifting that car seat and pushchair, and maybe looking after other children too! A lot is being asked of our bodies, which requires strength and stamina at a time when energetically we may be depleted. The great news is that there has been a big increase in the number of fitness professionals working specifically with the postnatal population and there are lots of fantastic programmes out there to help you navigate your return to exercise postpartum.

This progression in postnatal rehabilitation is juxtaposed against many of us having grown up in a society where we have been used to hearing language such as 'bouncing' or 'snapping' back and with that has brought a great deal of expectation around how we 'should' look aesthetically and what we expect our bodies to be physically able to do postnatally. I don't want to give these phrases too much prominence here, but it's really important to emphasise the effect and pressure this has brought upon us as new mums. It's time to ditch this rhetoric in favour of postnatal rehabilitation and recovery.

First of all, it's important to highlight that you will be, or you have been, pregnant for approximately nine months. As a postnatal personal trainer who has rehabilitated my own body and many of my clients', to give you a rough idea and to manage your expectations, it is realistically going to take a number of months (client-dependent) to rehabilitate your body. No two people will have the same level of fitness before becoming pregnant, no two pregnancies are the same and no two births are the same. From the moment we conceive, each of our physical journeys will take different trajectories and, for some mums, getting back to what they enjoy can feel infuriatingly slow and it is certainly not always linear. We need to progress smartly and shake off comparison. Rest assured that with the right programming and consistency, plus cutting yourself a little bit of slack, you will return to your exercise ambitions, hopefully stronger than ever before!

Even if women are experiencing postnatal issues, such as diastasis recti (abdominal separation), incontinence and prolapse, there are specific ways we adapt our rehabilitation and these symptoms are treatable.

In the early days, the first six weeks and maybe slightly longer if you had an abdominal birth, a tear or an episiotomy, the focus should well and truly be on healing and resting at every opportunity – easier said than done, I know, if your circumstances don't really permit this and you already have little ones around!

You can begin your pelvic floor exercises and diaphragmatic breathing within 24 hours of delivery (see page 99), although I appreciate these may not be top of the to-do list! As and when you feel able, you can also begin gentle core activation exercises, mobility work and postural awareness. You may receive some guidance on these exercises from the hospital or your midwife, or you can seek advice from a pelvic health physiotherapist, a postnatal personal trainer or the NHS website. Gentle movement, like short walks, is also great for the healing process. I encourage you to listen to your body and be guided by how you feel energetically each day, but just a short ten-minute walk/shuffle in the fresh air is really beneficial for the mind, body and soul!

Around six weeks postpartum, you will receive your postnatal check with your GP and, if possible, I would highly recommend requesting through your GP or privately booking a pelvic health check with a pelvic health physiotherapist. From experience, I understand that every postnatal GP check is slightly different and your GP may not check your diastasis recti or pelvic floor. Instead, it is more common for the focus of that appointment to be on mental well-being and the superficial healing of tears, episiotomies and caesarean scars. However, you can always ask for your GP to check your abdominal separation. It's worth highlighting that at six weeks, everyone will still have a degree of separation and mums should not be alarmed by that; it is a natural adaptation and your body is recovering every day. A more useful indication of how your diastasis is healing can be felt around three months postpartum.

Once you have attended your GP postnatal check, providing you have had an uncomplicated vaginal delivery and you feel ready physically and energetically (this may be slightly longer at around eight to ten weeks for abdominal births or if you have any other complications), you will be signed off by the GP to return to exercise.

So what does that mean? Unfortunately, the GP will not guide you on what exercise to return to and this can leave a lot of us assuming we've been given the green light to go straight back to the exercise we enjoyed pre-pregnancy or, conversely, feeling a bit lost and not knowing where to begin.

A very important aspect of your rehabilitation is firstly mastering functional movements. As our children grow, we also want to ensure we are progressing by consistently increasing challenge, load and resistance in these moves, so we are strong enough for mum life first and foremost. This applies to your core and also returning and building strength in functional movement patterns (squatting and lunging, pulling, pushing, rotating and carrying) – the movements mum life asks of us, repeatedly, every day. Think low-impact, though high-intensity is fine to challenge your cardiovascular endurance.

Introducing dynamic, explosive, high-impact and heavy movements are also areas which need a graded return. Thankfully, there are a number of personal trainers now who are qualified to train the postnatal population, who offer training in-person and online, and there are also a number of online postnatal-specific programmes available, so do seek out support.

CHAPTER 5

LOOKING AFTER YOURSELF

FACT

Having a tiny person to look after takes up an unreal amount of time.

BUT ALSO TRUE

You'll find ingenious ways to still care for yourself, learn how to set boundaries and prioritise yourself. Essential life skill acquired!

Think of your well-being, energy and health like a bank balance. Before kids, you were able to top it up regularly with uninterrupted sleep, time to exercise and prepare food, undisturbed time with friends, time alone to regroup – whatever floated your self-care boat. But now your well-being bank balance is seriously depleted: four hours' sleep in a row if you're lucky, one-handed shovelling of whatever snacks you can reach from wherever you're pinned under the baby, the ludicrous weight of responsibility to care for this tiny little human... that's a lot of withdrawals with no deposits to speak of.

In my experience, the best way to approach this is to come up with ways in which you can make teeny tiny deposits into your energy bank account – like taking the few pennies change after you've paid for something in the shop and putting it in a piggy bank. Just getting in the habit of making deposits, which can grow over time as the new baby dust settles, can make a huge difference to your health and well-being in the long term.

While you might be able to absorb the full impact of total dedication to your child for a few months, it will take its toll eventually. You'll do much better in the long run if you don't burn yourself out by falling victim to the self-sacrificial motherhood ideal we often get fed (in the media or through our own life experience). Long-term sleep deprivation and motherhood martyrdom can have a massive impact on your physical and mental health. You are way more likely to feel low, depressed or burnt out if you don't take steps to look after yourself and you will be more prone to infections and illnesses. When my eldest was one I had a sinus infection that wouldn't shift, swiftly followed by an inflammation somewhere behind my eye that made half my face puff up for weeks. In hindsight, I can see that I was so exhausted through chronic tiredness and unchecked anxiety about everything, it's no wonder I crumbled physically. I go through some simple examples of self-care below – pick the ones that jump out at you and feel doable. Something is always better than nothing.

'The first year might be exhausting physically, but the fatigue builds up and actually the toddler years are the hardest and most demanding, both physically and psychologically, especially when juggling motherhood, work and the commute. So prioritise self-care and don't be shy to ask for help to be able to save resource for longer.'

BUILD THE FOUNDATIONS

Let's start by stripping back self-care to the very basics – like drinking enough water, taking some deep breaths each day and being kinder to yourself. If you manage those reliably, you're already doing better than the majority of other people. And if you're reading this before giving birth, get those basics dialled in now. They're going to get you through the first few months and you can take comfort in having them as concrete habits already. Have a look back at your non-negotiables (page 50) and make sure you've added whatever super basic, preservation self-care you feel is doable for you and would help you to stay out of energetic bankruptcy.

PUT YOURSELF FIRST

I get it – this concept might feel impossible… To me, it felt both infuriating (I literally felt the dog was higher up on the priority list than me for a while) and almost impossible to achieve. The self-sacrifice we've been modelled by our own parents, the media, etc., has been strongly ingrained in us, which is why working out your priorities and non-negotiables cropped up so early on in the book. If you're really sure about the things you'd still like to prioritise for yourself, then you'll find/make/ask for the time. It's really that simple, and it's really important that you do.

Enlist help if you're struggling to put yourself first. If you find that the urge to do everything yourself is overpowering (and this does happen, even if, logically, you know that it's impossible and you really shouldn't even attempt it) and you find it hard to make time to rest and look after yourself, get someone to tell you. After my second baby, I instructed my husband to tell me to go and lie down whenever an opportunity presented itself. He knew that not resting enough would make my anxiety, and short fuse towards him, flare up, so it was in his best interests to make sure I didn't get too frazzled around the edges. And for me, it felt like permission to rest. And that did the trick. Someone else telling me to do it, allowed me to relax into resting, rather than seeing it as something that I knew I *should* do. This may not work for everyone, but it sure was a game changer for me.

One thing that has worked for lots of the mums I've spoken to, and worked with, is to plan one thing that's just for you each day. Knowing that you have one nice thing planned for yourself in the day can make all the difference and give you something to look forward to. This can be as small as making time for a few mahoosively deep breaths and a glass of water, or something chunkier like a half-hour nap, painting your nails or taking a walk by yourself while someone looks after baby.

Here's a piece of knowledge that makes total sense before you have a baby and then becomes the hardest thing ever once you're a mum: As long as baby is safe, it's OK to let them cry for a minute while you pour yourself a glass of water, go to the bathroom or even have a shower. Your basic self-care should take priority and short periods of upset are OK for the baby. But let me tell you – a baby's cry elicits a physical reaction like you wouldn't believe. Your mother brain is wired to respond to it no matter what and it can feel physically impossible to let your baby cry. Now, some babies are more laidback than others and you might be able to pop them in their little bouncy chair while you wash your hair, but a lot of them take great offence to this and are very vocal about letting you know.

The best way to take self-care action despite the visceral reaction to put baby first is to keep repeating to yourself that you're able to show up better as a mum and, most importantly, feel better within yourself, when your basic needs are met. Of course, I don't mean to let your baby cry for any prolonged amount of time, just a few minutes while you catch your breath and make yourself feel a little more human. And if you really can't hack it (I really couldn't with my first), a sling might be your friend – your baby will then be soothed and you'll have both hands free to do things for yourself.

'Your needs sometimes need to come before the baby and that's OK because if you're exhausted, depleted and struggling, you're going to be of very little help to your baby and unable to focus on them and meet their needs.'

TAKE TIME TO REST

We've all heard this one, haven't we: Sleep when the baby sleeps. The sentiment is lovely and you definitely should whenever you're able to (because everything is one thousand times worse when you're bone-tired), but it's hard, too, because if you don't have much help around, when will anything get done? I used to run around like a headless chicken every time my first went down for a nap. For months she slept for exactly 45 minutes. And each time I'd promise myself that I would get some rest, but somehow managed to fill exactly 40 minutes with chores, jump into bed, get comfy and jump right up again when she woke up. But I learnt my lesson – whenever I was home with baby number two, I would set a timer for 10 minutes, do whatever I could in that time and then rest until she woke up. This was a life-changing shift that I would highly recommend.

'I wish I'd been told (again and again) how important it is to keep looking after yourself too and not only baby/children, and, at the same time, if your baby falls asleep on you just stop everything and enjoy it!'

MY SELF-CARE TOP TIPS

Besides sleeping when the baby sleeps, below are a few super simple and realistic suggestions to get you started, arranged by what stage in baby land you're in. There's space to create your own list in the 'simple self-care reminders' planning space on page 74.

EARLY DAYS/TINY BABY SURVIVAL MODE

* Make sure you get a little bit of time to yourself each day, even if it's just for brushing your teeth or having a shower. Keep in the habit of being

your own person, on your own.

*   Remember to take a few deep breaths, drink a glass of water and eat something a few times a day.

*   Go out for a walk with baby in the pram/sling (fresh air and an outside perspective really are amazing). Of course, do this by yourself, too, if you're able to.

*   Wear only the comfiest clothes.

*   Use shower gels and creams with lovely smells.

*   Listen to a podcast or watch your favourite TV programme while you're feeding baby/stuck under a sleeping baby. Anything to remind you that there is life outside of baby care is a bonus.

*   Be as kind to yourself as you can possibly muster. Talk nicely to yourself; give yourself pep talks and mental high-fives. Be your own cheerleader.

*   Ask for help.

A LITTLE LATER

When baby is crawling, things can become a little more adventurous:

*   Find the perfect baby/toddler group where your child is happy, the coffee is good and there are some mums on a similar wavelength to chat to.

*   Take a few hours out by yourself, without baby – to the supermarket, for coffee or to just sit in the car in silence. It's all just so good.

*   Have a little stretch on the floor while baby eats lunch/watches TV/tries to put on a sock.

*   Book a treatment for yourself (and make sure you go!).

*   Carve out a little more time for hobbies and things that bring you joy. The added structure of mealtimes and possibly more predictable naps can help with this.

*   Hand over more childcare chores to others around you. The addition of mealtimes is perfect for this!

*   Ask for help.

A LITTLE LATER STILL

Once everyone has settled in a bit and hopefully sleeping a bit better:

* Have a night out/arrange dinner with a friend, and fight the temptation to talk about your kids all night. You'll be reminded that there is life after 8pm and you can be part of it!

* Start an exercise class or commit to some scheduled movement of sorts, or another hobby if exercise is not for you.

* Have a think about how you're nourishing yourself. Have any eating habits crept in that served a purpose while baby was tiny, but can now be overhauled? (There's NO pressure here, I just know that I didn't need a slice of carrot cake and five cups of coffee every day anymore once we all slept a little better.)

* Take a shopping trip (only rule: don't buy anything for anyone else, including the kids!).

* Ask for help.

BE COMPASSIONATE WITH YOURSELF

Above all, and in every stage, one of the most important things you want to get into the habit of doing is talking kindly to yourself, cutting yourself lots of slack and being accepting of, and patient with, yourself. It can be a ridiculously hard job being a mum. Don't add to that by being mean to yourself. Finding some kindness and compassion for yourself every day will go the furthest in supporting you on this mother of all journeys.

'It's not all about the baby! You need to take care of yourself, rest, sleep and eat well. I'd had an emergency caesarean, lost a lot of blood and felt awful. I was descended on every day by people who wanted to see the baby and felt tremendous pressure to look nice, have a tidy home, have the baby ready, etc. to receive visitors. Every time I tried to sleep, the doorbell would ring again. People don't realise how you feel unless you tell them. I was exhausted and frazzled. After my second child's birth I told my husband to keep the visitors to certain times and days.'

SIMPLE SELF-CARE REMINDERS

These'll come in handy, I promise. In the heat of the moment/sleep deprivation, it's really hard to think of the simple things you can do to look after yourself. Having it written down already means you won't need to tax your brain with decision-making.

✳ Favourite songs (pick a few different ones for different moods. Nothing resets like a fitting tune!):

✳ Favourite simple snack (have grab-and-go food that's satisfying handy at all times):

✻ One-handed/easy meals (more often than not, baby will decide that your dinner time is their party time. They have a sixth sense for timing, so it's good to have some quick, nutritious meals to hand):

....

....

....

....

....

....

✻ Places to go for fresh air:

....

....

....

....

....

....

'When I feel low on energy I will... ':
(Dance around the kitchen, drink some water, call a friend...)

....

....

....

....

....

....

'When I need calming down and soothing I will... ':
(Light a candle, take deep breaths, stretch...)

'When I feel overwhelmed I will... ':
(Breathe some more, make a list, talk about it...)

'When I feel angry I will... ':
(Investigate what's behind the anger, take a shower, get some fresh air...)

PROTECTING YOUR MENTAL HEALTH

Post-birth hormones are powerful beyond comprehension.

Your brain has gone through some stunning updates; you'll get to know yourself better than you ever have and the newborn/ new mum fog *will* lift.

First of all, some fascinating news: during pregnancy your brain receives a 'motherhood upgrade' and is now fine-tuned to keeping you and baby safe. And while that's very clever of your brain, it unfortunately hasn't quite adapted to modern-day living and we'll often act as if we might end up as lunch for a pre-historic predator. Since that's not the case, our hypervigilance can often end up over the top, and make us much more anxious and nervous than necessary. On the plus side, this brain upgrade makes you much better at identifying what your baby needs, because the part of your brain that works out what people are feeling and what they might need has wired much more closely together. But while you might be a hypervigilant ninja with a super close connection to your kid, you're also the clumsiest you've ever been and your memory is a thing of the past. Something had to give to fit those superhuman mum skills into that noggin! So, there you have it – baby brain is an actual thing!

Maternal brain development is an area that's only recently been studied in depth and is still lacking a lot of knowledge, but it's fascinating that we not only create new life, but also reshape our own brains to keep that life safe. Total superhero material.

THE BABY BLUES

While your brain goes all X-Men on you, your hormones take a bit more of a gung-ho approach. Already all over the place throughout pregnancy, they really send you on a ride after baby is born.

Around about three to five days after giving birth, what's called the 'baby blues' kicks in in so many women that this is now considered 'normal' by the NHS. But just because it's normal doesn't mean it's easy or can be glossed over. Your body goes through this massive hormone shift in a bid to readjust after birth and, as a result, you might be feeling extra touchy with a side of restlessness and anxiety. Tears will most likely be flowing freely and often for no apparent reason. Combined with sleep deprivation and trying to heal from birth, it can be an awful lot to hit you all at once.

Simply knowing that this is a thing that happens to almost everyone can be really useful and almost reassuring. Let it happen, get lots of extra help if you can and ride it out. The good news is that these intense emotions (and the swings of them) generally only last for a few days.

'You can possibly feel every emotion within the space of an hour!'

Below are some simple breathing exercises for when you need a reset, would rather not turn into 'shouty mum' or overwhelm threatens to swallow you up.

* *Elongating your out-breath.* This is the simplest of them all. Simply making your out-breath longer than your in-breath switches on the calming mechanism within your nervous system. If you would like to add some counting (it does add extra distraction, which can be quite useful), you could try breathing in for four counts and breathing out for eight. If that doesn't work for you, don't worry. I personally get anxious about counting a long out-breath because I worry that I won't be able to get there and that ruins the whole relaxation vibe.

* *Breathe and soften.* Breathe deeply and, on every out-breath, focus on releasing some tension within your body. Drop your shoulders away from your ears, soften your jaw, unclench your glutes, relax your fingers and toes, etc.

* *Box breathing.* This is a counting one, but they are short counts

and it works even for me! Breathe in for a count of four, hold your breath for four, breathe out for four, hold for four — and repeat. It surprises me each time I do it how calming it is!

* *Trace your fingers.* Take the index finger of one hand, place it at the outside edge of your thumb and breathe in as you slowly stroke your finger up the side of your thumb. Carry on tracing up and over the inside of the thumb as you breathe out on the way down. Breathe in on the way up the index finger, and so on. Physical touch is incredibly calming. Coupled here with breath, it's a double whammy.

* *Breathing walking meditation.* Another simple one, that is handy for when you're endlessly pushing or carrying a sleeping baby. Count your steps and synch your breath to them: three steps in, three steps out — or whatever works. Humming a matching tune is optional but brings added joy.

WHEN THE BABY BLUES BECOMES SOMETHING MORE

Baby blues is generally considered to happen during, and limit itself to, the first two weeks after giving birth. If feelings of anxiety, depression, low mood or hopelessness continue for more than two weeks, it might be a sign that something more serious is afoot and extra support is called for.

This is where conversations before having the baby come in handy: talk about how you normally deal with low mood, tiredness and frustration, and that way your partner and/or those around you can help spot behaviours and emotions that might be out of the ordinary for you, even in these new circumstances. There is a handy 'Protecting Your Mental Health' planning space on page 86 just for those conversations! Of course, it's never too late to have these chats, so get talking wherever you are on the motherhood path.

I won't go into too much detail on the kinds of mental health issues you may encounter, because that could fill a whole book on its own and I'm not qualified to do so. But I do want to mention that we're not just talking about postnatal depression (PND), but a sliding scale of mental health conditions and ways that mothers may struggle. It certainly isn't a case of 'you either have PND or you're finding everything easy'. There's a lot of grey area in between those two states (I'd argue that no one at all is actually in that second camp) and that's OK; grey is OK – it goes with everything. Below is a list of PND symptoms taken from the NHS website to give an idea of what to look out for in yourself or others:

* a persistent feeling of sadness and low mood
* lack of enjoyment and loss of interest in the wider world
* lack of energy and feeling tired all the time
* trouble sleeping at night and feeling sleepy during the day
* difficulty bonding with your baby
* withdrawing from contact with other people
* problems concentrating and making decisions
* frightening thoughts – for example, about hurting your baby

WHERE CAN YOU TURN TO FOR HELP?

Trusted friends and family can be great to confide in in the first instance. Talking about something is often an important first step to understanding and dealing with what's going on for you – it can feel like an actual weight is lifted, just by sharing. And, of course, those around you can only help you in the most optimal way if they know how you're feeling and what's on your mind. I'm still fairly certain that instead of antidepressants after having my second kid, I actually needed more help – actual, physical help; someone coming in a few times a week to keep me company and do a few chores. Without someone coming in to take the pressure off every now and again, the constant sense of having to be 'on' all the time was really overwhelming. Once the kids started going to childcare a few days a week, this eased considerably. Simply being your own person again and being able to think your own thoughts, uninterrupted, is so soothing.

Your health visitor and GP are also well-equipped to support and signpost you towards more specific help. On page 142 you'll find contact details for some larger organisations and charities that support the mental well-being of mothers, which can be an excellent point of contact, and certainly better than all the helplines (one a customer support line on the formula bottle that my baby wouldn't take) I rang after having my first; because I couldn't work out where to turn to, I turned to random places.

Luckily, times have changed and there is lots of support out there for mothers these days. The first place you look might not be right for you, but please keep looking. One size does not fit all and you deserve to have a nice, cosy fit for your mental health support. Keep trying different healthcare providers, counsellors, helplines, mums groups, etc., until you find what feels right for you. Not only will it help you feel better, but if it's the right fit, it won't feel like just another thing on your to-do list. The sense of feeling seen, heard and understood is priceless, and invaluable for your well-being in motherhood.

> *'Your brain just doesn't think the same way after having a baby, particularly in the first few months. I remember being petrified about taking my baby on the train in case I tripped and he fell on the track or I dropped him going down the stairs. I saw potential dangers in everything.'*

> *'Becoming a mum changes you as a person and it takes a while to come to terms with that.'*

BE HONEST

Admitting you're struggling with your mental health isn't failure, weakness or anything to be ashamed about. One in ten women in the UK are affected by PND, and that's not counting those who present with other conditions on the sliding scale we discussed above. No one will think you're an unfit parent. In fact, the opposite is true – everyone will want to support you, but they can only do that if you're honest about how you're feeling.

TALK

So talk, talk and talk some more – with those closest to you (and with the help of a pre-birth chat as outlined previously), with other mums and with healthcare professionals if necessary. If people don't know, or are unsure of, what's going on for you, they won't know how best to support you. So forget all about 'needing to cope by yourself' for some unknown, mysterious reason or, worse still, 'snap out of it'. People on your team will want to help and support you. Let them.

I remember having conversations with my husband about how I was feeling after having our first – the intrusive thoughts, the non-stop worrying, the restlessness, the guilt, never feeling like anything was enough. He was speechless. He had no idea that's what was happening in my head. He thought I'd turned into an unpleasant person overnight, because my anxiety manifested in anger and violent mood swings. That conversation marked such a turning point for us. It didn't necessarily make it easier, but there was more understanding, patience and goodwill.

In fact, you really can't start that talking journey early enough. It can be a really good idea to have a debrief from whatever your birth experience has been. Depending on what your experience was like, your NHS trust might offer you a debrief session, where you can also give feedback on the care you received. Your health visitor should be able to listen to you and offer any advice or referrals if necessary and a postnatal doula would gladly listen to your birth story and can most likely suggest counsellors who specialise in this area if needed. Do share your experience with other mums, too, if you feel able to; it really helps to get it all out in the open and know that you're not alone. In fact, I think the reason so many women tell each other scary birth stories (including inappropriately to pregnant friends) is because they haven't shared their experience enough to process it sufficiently.

THE GIST

Hormones can start you off on an emotional roller-coaster and there's lots of help and support available if this turns into something more than the baby blues.

CATHERINE NABBS

COUNSELLOR

For all the increased awareness of maternal mental health, there is still stigma around acknowledging that for many, many women this is not the blissful time we've been told to expect and may be eagerly anticipating. In addition, women are experts at masking, and when you combine this with the fear of judgement for not enjoying time with a sometimes longed-for baby, or imagined consequences of not being able to parent, the barriers to accessing mental health support become even more apparent.

One of the first things to develop, ideally while you are pregnant, is an attitude of curiosity and compassion. We are bombarded with external expectations – from family, friends, movies, social media, magazines... the list is endless – and in the noise of 'Oh, you must be so happy', 'I'm sure you'll be super organised' and 'You're going to be such a great mum', your own fantasies, thoughts, doubts, feelings and expectations can be drowned out. Spending time on your own, reflecting on how you really feel can be so useful.

Notice how you feel about being pregnant – are you feeling invaded, clinging on to pre-baby normal life for as long as possible, or are you more inward-looking and friendly towards the changes taking place in your body? There is no judgement here – both extremes and everywhere in between are normal responses to what is a massive shift.

Perhaps try to notice what feelings the expectations of becoming a parent bring up in you; becoming aware of your own childhood and how you were handled as a baby can be really helpful with this (see also page 29 and 34). It may explain the way you are relating to your baby and any difficulty you have in handling or bonding, and allows space for self-compassion. Bringing these thoughts into awareness allows for more choices and the possibility to parent more intentionally.

It's helpful to become familiar with some simple breathing exercises; these help to lower your baseline of anxiety, thereby extending your capacity to cope with the ever-increasing demands on your time, body and relationships (see page 79).

It is also important to recognise that with every change comes an element of loss. Even with an ideal birth and a healthy baby, you are no longer pregnant... sounds obvious I know, but it can be difficult for some mothers to relinquish the exquisite intimacy of being pregnant — that beautiful bubble of two. In order to move forward and fully experience joy in the moment, we have to be allowed to acknowledge and feel the loss of the stage that came before.

I know it's been mentioned before, but I don't think I can overstate the significance of being able to debrief after you've given birth. The body can experience even the most 'normal' birth as a trauma — remember, this is the first time you have given birth, or even if you've already had a baby, this will be a different birth; no two are the same — and the way we process trauma is by talking about it, over and over, and allowing ourselves to re-experience and normalise the feelings we have about it.

When we are struggling with our mental health, there is a tendency to retreat and become isolated. Please notice if you feel this happening to you and give yourself permission to reach out and connect in whatever way feels comfortable to you — as well as friends and family, there are support groups and mental health practitioners who can offer the level of connection and support that you need.

PROTECTING YOUR MENTAL HEALTH

Sit down with your partner, other close caregiver and/or someone who knows you well and come up with a list of things to look out for within yourself and each other in terms of your mental health:

* What might be a sure-fire sign of trouble? What behaviour(s) can you look out for, in each other?

....

....

....

....

....

....

* How do you normally cope with stress?

....

....

....

....

....

....

✱   What coping tools do you currently rely on when feeling stressed out or overwhelmed?

_____

_____

_____

_____

_____

✱   Will those coping tools still be available to you in early motherhood?

_____

_____

_____

_____

_____

✱   How might it look when you're at capacity/breaking point?

_____

_____

_____

_____

_____

_____

✳   Who or what can help to take the pressure off when capacity is reached or exceeded?

....
....
....
....
....
....
....
....

✳   Are there any traits you're already familiar with that could become aggravated by sleep deprivation and change (anxiety, OCD, depression, etc.)?

....
....
....
....
....
....
....
....

RESPECTING YOUR BODY

Your body changes a lot throughout and after pregnancy, and it can take quite some time to recover.

You've grown an entire human and your body is literal magic.

It's taken nine months (or thereabouts) to grow an actual person from scratch. And while pregnant, everyone coos over you and your bump, making you feel special and extraordinary (unless you're having an uncomfortable pregnancy in which case the attention can still be nice but is more likely to be annoying). Yet once baby is born, all that magic is seemingly forgotten and you're expected to bounce back and look as if you were never pregnant – often within a matter of days. Let's call collective bullshit on that and normalise a healthy healing journey in your own sweet time.

If you look hard enough in your pregnancy books and probe a little during your antenatal classes, you might unearth some facts about postpartum recovery, but often the information is sparse and the baby is the sole focus. As long as the baby's healthy, that's the main thing, right? Well, guess what – your health, well-being and postnatal recovery matter too.

While the following is by no means an exclusive list, they were things that cropped up again and again when I asked nearly 500 mums what they would like to have known about the physical recovery after birth. If you'd rather skip past this chapter, go for it. You might feel that knowing too much about things that might not even happen would make you too worried or anxious, which is an absolutely legitimate point. My main concern when planning and writing this book has always been that I don't want to pop anyone's 'pregnancy bubble'. You can always come back to this chapter some other time, but I would recommend you read the fantastic section from the women's health physio on page 96 before you move on.

STRAIGHT AFTER GIVING BIRTH

Labour unfortunately isn't finished once the baby is born (sorry) — there are a few more stages to go through. The placenta has to make its way out, which in some cases is super swift, while in others it takes a little while. (The midwife during my second birth victoriously presented my placenta like it was the beginning of the *Lion King* to the rest of the ward and everyone cheered!) Then your uterus begins to retract fairly soon after birth, often kick-started by the first breastfeed. Some people hardly feel this (I was one of the lucky ones), while for others it feels like contractions all over again.

I go into more detail about breastfeeding in Chapter 8 (page 101), but I just want to add here that if you are going to give breastfeeding a go, the time straight after labour can feel a little overwhelming in that regard. While you're trying to recover from labour, and possibly an element of surgery or medical intervention, you've also got to try to work out how to latch baby on for their first feed. This in itself can be tricky because it is all new to you, yet you've been told it's so natural and should be easy. Most hospitals will have staff on hand to help you and hopefully they'll sort you and baby out. If, however, they're short-staffed or rushed or you feel like they are not patient or gentle enough with you, speak up. I felt like I was treated a little roughly and made to feel as if I should have known what to do. It took me a little while to get over that and I wish I'd asked for someone different to show me the ropes.

Initially, you might not make enough milk beyond the magical colostrum that your body produces first. For me, baby latched on OK, but wouldn't stop feeding (she'd scream every time I tried to remove her). I'd read so many parenting books that urged you to be careful to not become a 'human dummy' if you're breastfeeding, that I was already scared of that happening. Looking back, I could slap myself for thinking that. But I digress.

Your milk coming in can feel a little painful at first as your breasts become engorged (I mean, just that word makes me feel uncomfortable...) and establishing feeding can also feel physically painful with sore, cracked nipples a distinct possibility. Again, there is help available to help make things as comfortable for you as quickly as possible, so do reach out to the experts.

Less major, but still quite an event, is going for your first wee! It'll be your first encounter with your post-birth private parts and they'll be rather swollen and bruised, possibly with stitches (which can happen through a C-section, of course, but also from a repaired natural tear or an episiotomy incision during an assisted delivery). Remember, things won't stay this way, so don't panic. Your wee will sting on any grazes. (Top tip here: have a jug with lukewarm water ready (or a squeezy sports bottle) to water down your stream. I got quite used to doing this and actually quite liked it!) If you can time your first wee with your first shower, even better. Number twos are a concern for similar reasons — everything down below is sore and, if you've had stitches, the pressure of passing a poo can be a lot. Drink plenty of water and pack some dried fruit in your hospital bag to keep things moving smoothly.

IF YOU'VE HAD A C-SECTION

Recovery from a C-section will look different and potentially take longer than a vaginal birth. In fact, it might be an awesome idea to make an 'in case I have a C-section' plan. You'll be recovering from fairly significant surgery, unable to move freely or lift anything heavy. Would this make the first six weeks of motherhood very different to what you're hoping for? Would someone need to take extra time off work to offer more help? Or maybe you can enlist someone who can drive you and the baby places (not that you have to go anywhere! Stay home and comfy if you can!).

> Whatever you do, do not overdo it, keep hydrated and eat as well as you can manage (this massively helps healing and the way your scar forms). Keep an eye on your scar and, if anything seems off, don't hesitate to get someone to have a look for you.

Take deep breaths into your abdomen as soon as this feels comfortable. It helps everything to find its place again after baby has made some space and helps stretch the tissue layers, which in turn helps your scar assemble in the best way.

Give your tummy some love. Very often when women didn't anticipate a C-section, they become disconnected with this part of their body and don't look at, or touch, their scar. If you're at all able to, place your flat hands lightly over your tummy, near your scar if you can, and simply send some kindness and acceptance to this part of you. Sounds a bit 'out there' I know, but you'd be surprised by how powerful it can be.

ONCE YOU GET HOME

Again, a myriad of things might or might not happen, but these are some of the ones I and other mums wished we'd known!

Stock up on those maternity pads, because the bleeding after birth continues for some time. It can take up to five or six weeks to stop and if you think it's stopped earlier than that, you might find you start again if you've had a more active day than usual.

Your pelvic floor has been under just a tad of pressure for the last nine months. Some form of leaking or being unable to hold your wee for any stretch of time can be quite normal for the days and weeks after giving birth, while everything retracts back to where it might have been pre-baby. I'll leave the more detailed pelvic floor advice to the expert voice at the end of this chapter (see page 96).

With the hormone changes after birth come so many wonderful gifts (we've covered the tears, the anger and the rage already), including night sweats. I'd wake up drenched for night feeds, needing a complete pyjama change (sometimes even the sheets). Just another thing to deal with in the middle of the night!

And if you think the sweats, the leaking and the bleeding were bad enough, we're about to *really* go there – piles. No one told me about piles! You might escape them completely, they might pop by for a visit while you're pregnant and constipated/after pushing the baby out, or they might stick around forever. Nice one. Thanks Mother Nature.

While some of these can be unpleasant and, let's be frank, really flipping unfair and annoying, it's never just you going through this. It happens to others, too, it's normal and, through the power of the Internet, we can search for all sorts of weird and wonderful ways that might help a little, and find some much-needed solidarity while we're at it.

FURTHER INTO RECOVERY

As you recover, your body goes through so many changes all over again. It takes time for extra fluid to filter out of your body, for your tummy to deflate and your ribcage to sink back to where it was pre-pregnancy. Once your body has gone through some of this re-adjustment, you'll be able to see which parts of your pregnancy journey stay with you more permanently, like stretchmarks or loose skin on your tummy. Contrary to popular belief, nothing you use to moisturise your skin will dramatically change the way it appears. Yes, eating well and staying hydrated help, but they won't make your tummy look like you've not had kids unless you're genetically predisposed to have super supple skin that pings back into shape without any signs of stretchage (technical term that).

It might be at this stage that you'll think about returning to exercise, and you can explore the tips from our expert voice on page 96.

'Some people bounce back, but others take a long time to heal. I felt a mess physically afterwards with my stretch marks and loose skin. I felt so unprepared for it.'

'I have a different brain (and different priorities). A different vagina, hips and ribcage. My shoulders are wider, the same with my feet. Even though I weigh less and have less body fat than before I ever got pregnant, my clothes (and shoes) don't fit.'

KEEP ASKING FOR THE RIGHT SUPPORT

Have you spotted a theme yet? Keep asking healthcare professionals whenever something doesn't feel right; from breastfeeding and how you're healing physically, to your mental health. And if you don't get what you need straight away, keep on pushing and keep on asking. You might have a brilliant health visitor and/or GP, but there are unfortunately still some who fall into the 'You're a mum now, that's just how it is' category, and you don't have to stand for it.

Things like abdominal separation and various types of prolapse are really common and women are often made to believe that they're also normal — but that's not so. There is lots that can be done to get you feeling well in your own skin again. There's a resource section for you to complete at the end of the book, which includes space to note down your local women's health physio (page 144). If you're struggling with recovery and the GP doesn't refer you, that's the kind of person you might want to seek out.

BUY COMFY POSTPARTUM CLOTHING

Straight up comfort should come before anything else in the first few months. If you are breastfeeding, shirts or tops with buttons are handy, as is double-layering a vest under any old top, and there are now so many nifty breastfeeding tops and dresses around (but also, you might grow used to just whipping a boob out...). Definitely, under no circumstances, get anything that needs ironing.

Get extra-cosy pyjamas for night feeds and have some cardigans, pashminas (are they still a thing?) or scarves handy to cover up if it's chilly. Adding little touches to make you feel just a little more comfortable and cared for will honestly make a huge difference.

THE GIST

There are many physical changes during pregnancy and the recovery afterwards. Give yourself time. And ask for help when something doesn't feel right.

AISHLING BURKE

WOMEN'S HEALTH PHYSIO

The fourth trimester (the three months after giving birth) is a time for recovery and reconnection with your amazing body that has worked so hard for the best part of the last year.

I use the word 'recover' as I truly believe we need to help women heal and rehabilitate after childbirth, but alas currently this doesn't happen very often. If you injured your knee, you would see a physio to help decrease pain, improve movement and return to full function. Well, guess what, that's what women's health physios do for the pelvic floor!

The initial period after having a baby is often a blur of feeds, changing nappies, sleep deprivation and grabbing whatever you can find to pop in your mouth before your little one 'calls' for Mamma again. Think of these early days as an opportunity to reconnect with your posture, pelvic floor and breathing. You don't need equipment or even need to get 'down onto the floor'; just a little focus and a few breaths is enough.

There is so much to talk about, but I'll highlight the two pertinent points that I cover with new mums on our first postpartum consultation: breathing and the pelvic floor.

BREATHING

I know, we all do it and have never given it a second thought, but do you know that your diaphragm (that large muscle that sits under the ribs) can get shunted up some 4cm during the latter stages of pregnancy (remember those days of getting out of breath quickly with just taking a few steps)? We need to encourage this band of muscle to start moving correctly again, not just because it's a little higher up than normal, but because it forms the most wonderful structure within our bodies — a structure we often talk about but don't know a great deal about… the core.

The core comprises of the diaphragm at the top, the pelvic floor at the bottom, the deep abdominal muscles at the front and some of the spinal muscles at the back. All too often, our focus on 'core strengthening' is doing lots of ab work and we often neglect the vital diaphragm at the top.

So how do you exercise it? Well, you breathe… better!

Breathing correctly lays the foundation for restoring and reconnecting your inner core as well as encouraging rest and calm. Diaphragmatic breathing encourages the diaphragm to move properly and 'kick-start' the core into gear after having a baby. Try the technique below little and often throughout the day to help get your core working as a unit again:

1. Sitting or lying down comfortably, place one hand on your chest and one on your tummy.

2. When you inhale, allow your tummy to rise as your lungs fill with air.

3. Visualise the diaphragm moving down as you breathe in (inhale) and coming up as you breathe out (exhale).

4. When you exhale, feel your belly contract as your diaphragm moves upwards.

Try to spend a little time each day in this comfy position. Diaphragmatic breathing sets the stage for re-engaging the core in a gentle, low-impact way (and the plus side is that it helps reduce stress, blood pressure and heart rate, and generally provides a feeling of well-being).

THE PELVIC FLOOR

The pelvic floor muscles are a group of muscles that are located within the pelvis attaching to the pubic bone at the front, the tailbone (coccyx) at the back and the sit bones (ischial tuberosities) that you might be perched on now as you read this. The main function of the pelvic floor is to support the bladder, bowel and uterus, manage abdominal pressures and provide stability to the pelvis and spine.

Pregnancy and childbirth ask a lot from our pelvic floor muscles, so it's important that we look to rehabilitate them soon after baby has arrived. Vaginal delivery adds considerable stretching and strain to these muscles, but that doesn't mean that abdominal delivery mammas don't need to reconnect and strengthen their pelvic floor too. Nine months of carrying a baby, changes in posture, hormonal changes and weight gain all add strain to the pelvic complex and some 70 per cent of pregnant women will report leakage with coughs or sneezes even before baby has arrived.

HOW TO LOCATE YOUR PELVIC FLOOR

The pelvic floor can be a bit of an enigma for many and often the first time we hear of the pelvic floor or exercising it is during pregnancy or postpartum. Locating and engaging the muscles can be particularly tricky after childbirth, but your technique will improve over time. Think of it like the brain speaking English while the pelvic floor is speaking French. Initially, a little is lost in translation, but with a little practice you and your pelvic floor will become firm friends!

All too often, we are so keen to build up strength that we 'throw the kitchen sink at it'– often becoming a 'glute gripper' (overusing the buttock muscles) or a 'tummy tucker' (sucking in the abdominal muscles). While on paper this sounds OK, we need to encourage the reactivation of the pelvic floor. A cue or phrase often helps as it focuses the mind on where exactly we want to lift, hold and importantly relax. Good cues include:

* Squeeze and lift the back passage (anus) as if trying to hold onto wind... and relax.

* Zip from back to front (pull the zip from the anus to the pubic bone)... and relax.

* Imagine you are trying to draw a blueberry up inside the vagina... and relax.

* Imagine you are trying to stop an imaginary wee... and relax.

HOW TO EXERCISE YOUR PELVIC FLOOR

Pelvic floor exercises can be performed anywhere in any position, but often after having a baby it's good to get into a position where you are relaxed, well-supported and can focus in on these muscles. Some women like to start in lying or side-lying. Lying is often regarded as easier by most and can be a good place to start in your pelvic floor journey. Work up to sitting (if breastfeeding, the pelvic floor automatically starts activating so this is a great opportunity to work it a little more), while being upright in standing can be challenging at first as you are not only working against gravity but your own body weight too. Don't sweat this too much if you can't 'feel' very much in standing; with practice your contraction will become better and better.

Try the following exercise:

* *Long holds.* In whichever position you choose, take a breath in to prepare, breathe out through the mouth while you squeeze your back passage as if holding onto wind (or whatever cue – see above – works for you). Try to maintain this contraction for eight to ten seconds as you continue breathing. Be mindful of fully relaxing the muscle at the end of the contraction. Try to aim for ten repetitions, three times daily.

* *Quick lifts.* Now for the quickies! Use your cue (so squeeze your back passage and hold onto wind) and release. Breathe throughout and aim for ten repetitions.

Holding a contraction for eight to ten seconds can be a big ask for some women early in postpartum recovery, so don't fret if you can only hold it for two to three seconds initially. Like someone training for a marathon, you have to build up strength and endurance. Research suggests that it can take anywhere up to 12 months to develop strong, flexible pelvic floor muscles. It will take time, but persevere!

WHO TO ASK FOR HELP IF SOMETHING DOESN'T FEEL RIGHT

Seeking assistance postpartum should be a right and not a request. If something doesn't feel right, don't be embarrassed or afraid to speak up, go back, get a second opinion or seek out the help of a pelvic health physiotherapist. We can assess, treat and rehabilitate postnatally. We can be found working within the NHS (your GP can refer you) or in private practice (check out the Squeezy app 'directory' for local pelvic health/women's health physiotherapists in your area).

CHAPTER 8

BONDING WITH YOUR BABY

FACT

You might not bond immediately.

BUT ALSO TRUE

That love will come. And it'll grow and grow and change and grow. Deeper and stronger.

The expectation, going into motherhood, is that we'll feel a rush of unconditional love as soon as we see the little person we've grown inside us, and that that's what's going to get us through the sleep deprivation and the rough bits at the start. While that's true for many people, it certainly isn't for everyone. I remember having my newborn on my chest straight after birth and it all feeling very surreal. I felt very little besides the realisation that her little leg felt exactly the same shape as I had felt through my tummy in the previous days. I kept repeating 'that's her leg, that's her leg' in my head and my mind was totally blown by this on a logical level, but there was no rush of love.

And it makes sense, right? **You need some time to get to know this new human and they need time to get to know you.**

And there are *so many* things to get used to, and you *will* get used to them. All the nappy changes, feeds, burpings, soothings and other endless chores of looking after a baby will become normal to you (and even routine-like at some point!) and it won't feel overwhelming forever. There'll always be moments, but the dust will settle. You might not like it all, but you'll cope with all of it.

> '*Bond and love are different things. All will be well (in fact joyous) in the end.*'

While you're trying to find your feet in motherhood and parenting, the steepness of the learning curve is going to throw you off-balance from time to time. In this chapter, I've included the most common issues that blind-sided the mums I've spoken to, but there'll no doubt be things that are specific to your unique situation. No matter what it is though, never, ever think that you're the only one feeling a certain way or going through a particular mothering conundrum. There are always other mums who can relate, have been there before or at the very least know where you're coming from. If in doubt – reach out!

YOU'RE WIRED TO NOT IGNORE YOUR BABY'S CRY

It's handy to know that a baby's cry can elicit a proper, physical reaction from you that can be totally overpowering and impossible to ignore, which is how the whole vicious cycle of mums doing the lion's share of parenting generally starts (as we saw on page 28). We physically can't cope with hearing the baby cry so we respond quicker, and hence condition ourselves, and those around us, that we're the first responders.

And not only do babies cry loudly, they cry a lot! This can be for many reasons – they are hungry, cold, warm, tired, scared, frustrated, overwhelmed, something hurts, a label is scratchy, etc. – and sometimes for no reason at all.

So that you don't get stuck in the primary caregiver loop forever and ever, it's an excellent idea to instruct others to react as quickly as you or, if you're by yourself, find ways to still look after your own well-being while baby is upset. The simple breathing exercises on page 79 are a good start since they can be done in the moment, without any effort needed. It sounds naff, I know, but some deep breaths really can help to increase your tolerance to cope with whatever is going on.

Often baby will simply just want to be close to you, especially in the first few months after being born. A sling can be your best friend during this time – and double-whammy winner: baby might settle and you've got your hands free to eat, hydrate or scroll for some distraction!

A lot of times you will have checked and checked again that baby is fed, burped, warm enough/not too hot and clean, and still they're upset. There's quite simply not always something you can do, as these mums put it perfectly:

> *'Sometimes your child might be sad or cross and you won't know why, but just accepting that and being there for what they need is*

a great thing to do. You will go crazy if you try to find a reason for everything.'

'Sometimes there isn't an answer; you just need to be there for your baby'.

YOU MIGHT GET ANGRY

At times, you might get very, very angry. And swear. At your baby. You'll think thoughts about your baby (and maybe your partner, too) that you never even knew you had in you. This can be really scary and such a shock, but it's totally normal (I really wish someone had told me this!). It doesn't mean you'll act on those thoughts; you're simply showing a variety of reactions to tough situations (while sleep-deprived and overwhelmed). (While it can be absolutely normal to have these thoughts and feelings, if at any point you feel like anger or harmful thoughts are getting the better of you, or you feel in any way inclined to act on your thoughts, then it's time to seek extra support.)

If you find yourself venting by shouting at those nearest and dearest to you, that's normal, too. It's natural that you let your anger and frustration out on those you feel safest with. This doesn't mean that it's OK, but it does help to explain a lot. Talking comes in handy once again, both to explain what's going on for you and work out a way to cope better going forwards. I'll often give my husband a warning that I'm feeling on the edge and to expect an outburst at any minute. Often that diffuses the anger, just by airing it. And sometimes it still erupts but doesn't feel as painful for the recipient.

YOU MIGHT NOT WANT TO LEAVE YOUR BABY

In a mind-boggling motherhood twist, when the time comes to get your child settled into nursery, or they're simply staying with relatives for a few hours while you nap, see friends or pop into work for half a day, it's going to be so hard to leave them. You might have wished for some time by yourself for months, but, when it arrives, you have no idea what to do with yourself.

When that time comes, I suggest you (re)read Chapter 10 on mum guilt, and then make a plan for your alone time. Actually, write down what you'd like to do ahead of time so that you don't feel so lost. Obviously, if you're headed to work or a doctor's appointment that's not quite the same, but you could still make a plan for your commute or what magazine you'll read in the waiting room. Plans are good, for our brains are sieve-like.

EVERYTHING IS A PHASE

This isn't an overused parenting cliché for nothing. Things really *do* shift and change *all* the time. A phase of night wakings or teething *might* seem like it lasts forever and you'll resign yourself to waking up six times a night for the rest of your life, but it will pass. The best quote I've ever seen said, 'It might pass like a kidney stone, but it will pass.' Ha!

> *'Keep repeating "it's only a phase". Every day/week/month I'd become fixated on something the baby would/wouldn't do (sleep/self-settle/feeding routines). It all feels relentless in the moment, but to know that it's all only a phase is a comfort — you always come out the other side. Eventually.'*

Just when you think you can't possibly go on and are too tired to take another step, your baby smiles at you for the first time, sleeps a little better or learns a new skill, like shaking a rattle or stacking some blocks. And those things will blow your mind and heart right open and enable you to carry on.

If you like routine, the fact that things change all the time can be tricky to deal with. For you, I have this comforting thought — eventually the phases stick around a little longer, naps become more predictable and you'll have regular groups/classes you go to, etc. It won't feel rudderless forever and a routine of sorts will emerge.

> *'The relentlessness of it is hard to come to terms with. I remember saying to a friend that it was actually quite hard in the days when they're too young to react to anything — once the smiling kicked in it was easier. Before that, the lack of response is surprisingly difficult. Of course you understand that a newborn can't do anything, but the emotional reality of the 24/7 cycle of feeding, changing, getting to sleep for no feedback, as it were, is incredibly wearing!'*

One of my favourite parenting mantras I've grown to love is: *Do what works until it doesn't.*

Let's chuck that 'making a rod for your own back' saying in the bin for good. It's not helpful and it's untrue. A way to change things will always appear once you've grown out of doing things a certain way; either your baby will tell you by no longer cooperating, or you'll be over doing things a certain way, at which point you'll rethink and try something new.

> *'Everything changes so quickly and that's normal. You get into a routine for it to have to change. Go with it... so much of what books say makes you concerned your routine isn't normal. But in fact anything is basically normal for a baby.'*

> *'Try not to worry about what will happen further down the line. "Making a rod for your own back" is one of the worst phrases for new mums; it's hard enough as it is in the moment, without worrying that what you're doing will have a negative effect at a later date. Do what you need to and want to in the moment and what feels right.'*

> *'It doesn't matter — you can fix things in your own time so you don't have to do everything "right".'*

Routines aren't all they're cracked up to be anyway. They can be super limiting if your baby will only sleep in their cot, at certain times of the day. I had an antenatal class friend who I really liked but never saw because our babies' nap schedules didn't match up. Tragic!

> *'A solid routine isn't always a great thing as they can get too used to it and it's then difficult to do anything outside of that. Go out and about and get them used to it as much as poss while they're still quite portable!'*

ALLOW YOURSELF TIME TO ADJUST

I've said it before and I'll say it plenty more times: give yourself time and cut yourself all the slack you can muster. It's all brand new and it's a lot. Allow yourself lots and lots of time and space to get used to being a mum, whatever that looks like in your situation and whatever it feels like, too. Don't rush things; feel things out, let them settle. You'll find things out about yourself (and your baby) over the course of the first few months that will influence how you feel about and deal with motherhood (and life in general). You don't have to know everything all at once. Let it all come together (and sometimes fall apart to come together again) over time.

BE KIND TO YOURSELF

Most importantly, be really, really kind to yourself. When you're overwhelmed – by tiredness, the amount of crying, the whole situation – give yourself tons of self-compassion. Meaning that whatever you do, don't talk so harshly to yourself in your own head. Don't tell yourself off and don't berate yourself. Imagine instead what you'd say to a good friend in your situation and channel that response into your own reactions and inner monologue. Give yourself pep talks, acknowledge that it's hard but that you can do it, and find kind words for yourself.

Try soothing gestures too when you're feeling emotional. Give your upper arms and shoulders a squeeze to mimic a hug, massage your hands or put a hand to your heart as the ultimate supportive gesture. These are the kinds of things that will support you in the long run and keep you on an even keel to enable you to support your less emotionally regulated newborn – not telling yourself off or constantly wishing you were doing better/ differently. Be your own cheerleader and have your own back. And if you need to hear external reassurances to help you along and supplement that not-so-kind voice in your head, make sure to ask those around you to provide that for you.

I've reminded my husband countless times that I need to hear what a good mum I am from him every now and again. I've got the kind self-talk sorted, but nothing beats hearing it from someone else sometimes.

As I mentioned earlier, we all hit our motherhood groove at different times. I was terrified for much of the first year and didn't really begin enjoying it until my kids started talking.

This didn't hinder me bonding with them or developing a relationship, it just became different (and more fun for me) when they got that little bit older. Other people cherish the time when babies can't move around yet and feel challenged by the toddler stage when they won't stand still. It's all good and normal.

There'll be good days and bad days, but mostly it'll be a mix of both — all the emotions one after another, sometimes at breakneck speed. It really is quite something.

THE GIST

Time, patience and kindness are key while you're getting to know your baby and your new motherhood self.

BONUS SECTION

`FACT`

Breastfeeding can be really tough (and painful).

`BUT ALSO TRUE`

There's tons of help available and it's OK to change your mind on your preferred way to feed.

I won't go into any detail on caring for your baby here, including feeding, since the focus of this guide is meant to be on you. Hopefully, whatever antenatal classes you have taken/ will take, plus parenting books, will cover a lot of the practical baby care topics at length. And there is lots of local support available for feeding issues wherever you are – there's a little black book section on page 144 for you to complete.

However, in the research for this book, so many mothers commented that they would have liked to have known how tricky breastfeeding could be, rather than simply being told that it was the best and most natural way to feed a baby, so I just wanted to add a few points here. I can't go into all the detail as it would be its own book, but there are a few things I'd like to give you a heads-up about, and you can find more information as and when it applies to you (which it might never!). As with everything else, keep looking for information and support until you've found what feels right for you.

It takes time to establish breastfeeding, and for it to become easy. While it can take a while for milk production to catch up with demand, your nipples can become cracked and sore in the process. Things like blocked milk ducts and mastitis are also common and can complicate your feeding journey. I know this sounds pretty grim, and it really can be a painful process with some stumbling blocks initially, but eventually things should settle down and, as always, there's support available to help you on your way.

Sleep and feeding your baby (whichever way you choose to feed) will dominate the first few weeks of newborn life. Your baby will need feeding every two hours and it really rather dominates the schedule!

Cluster feeding is a thing. I'd never heard of this before and was on the verge of tears when my baby wanted to feed non-stop for a couple of hours before settling down to sleep in the evening. A quick google threw up this term and that it's totally normal – and that's all I needed to know. I could then relax and deal with it, knowing that nothing was wrong. Dealing with it involved being fed snacks and watching box sets!

I was lucky that breastfeeding was literally the only thing that came easily to me in motherhood. It worked from Day 1 and I never had any issues, so much so that neither of my kids ever took a bottle. On the one hand, this was amazing because boobs are a magic wand to calm and soothe and make babies feel better, and it really is special to be able to provide that, but equally, I didn't leave the house for longer than two hours for months. I'm not sure I realised quite how exhausting this was at the time. You look back at a lot of things in early motherhood and think 'How did I ever get through that?' You do, somehow, but that doesn't mean it's easy. Effectively, I was a human dummy for the best part of two years (twice!) and that really does take it out of you. Luckily, that physical strain of the early months eases over time, to be replaced by more emotional challenges – remember, everything is a phase!

DON'T SUFFER ALONE OR IN SILENCE

Yup, it's that old chestnut again – find support. Your health visitor might have their specialty in breastfeeding support so they're a good first port of call, but there are plenty of independent breastfeeding counsellors and lactation consultants who can either come to your home or host support groups within your community (bonus: they tend to have biscuits and coffee and there are other people to chat to). I went to a few breastfeeding groups just for company and to have something to do. They were so welcoming!

There's online support, too, of course, which can often be enough if you just need to know you're not on your own. Facebook groups and baby forums can be great for this, but use these with caution – don't get sucked into the drama! They can offer really helpful perspectives from people who are going through the same stages as you or have been there and got the spit-stained muslin cloth to prove it. Just whatever you do, don't compare yourself!

YOU HAVEN'T 'FAILED' IF YOU DON'T BREASTFEED

Breastfeeding is made to look so natural and superior everywhere, and I have seen so many mums crumble and beat themselves up for months, if not years, for ending their breastfeeding journey earlier than they had planned (or for not considering it an option for themselves in the first place). They feel such shame around this perceived failure that it sours the rest of their motherhood experience. While I can't erase any of that, I'm hoping that simply making you aware of this possibility prepares you enough to not do this to yourself if you find yourself in that situation. As well as choosing what's best for baby, you also have to choose what's best for you.

Which brings me to the final and most important note of all to end this chapter:

> *'Your baby loves you, no matter what kind of job you think you're doing.'*

THE GIST

You are the right mum for your baby. Just as you are.

CHAPTER 9

SLEEPING: YOU AND YOUR BABY

`FACT`

You've never known tiredness like it.

`BUT ALSO TRUE`

You can function on incredibly little sleep, you *will* sleep again and there are ways to get you through this stage in one (slightly dishevelled and tired, but functioning) piece.

The obsession with sleep — my own to some extent, but the baby's mostly — is what surprised me most in motherhood. With my first, I essentially moulded my entire life around her sleep needs. I'd engineer trips in the car if she needed to catch up on some ZZZs (the car was the only sure-fire way she'd get a long nap in), plan any outing and holiday travel times around when she needed to sleep and stuck religiously to bedtime routines (still do!). I know this seems obsessive, but on the flipside is a fractious baby who is harder to settle down and way more emotional than a well-rested one. It's a really tough balance to strike.

While it wasn't for me, there are plenty of people who are more than happy to go with the flow, let baby sleep whenever it happens and enjoy the flexibility that brings. As with everything, try things out, see how it works for you and stick with what feels right for now.

A QUICK WORD ON PARENTING BOOKS

The amount of books, articles and blogs on the subject of baby sleep is immense. And I read all of them, in the hope that one would contain the key to longer naps and eight hours' sleep a night. But all they did was create more pressure to have a baby who would settle themselves to sleep and fit into a neat routine.

And while it felt good to be informed — to learn about sleep regressions and baby's brain development — the suggestion that any one book is able to tell you how best to ensure adequate rest for everyone in your family is bogus. It created unnecessary pressure because I felt things should be, or certainly *could* be, different. Calmer. Better. Easier (imagine a rolling eyes emoji right about here). Baby should be able to go X amount of hours between feeds, nap at the same time every day and settle to sleep well after a predictable evening routine. The thought of some sort of schedule, predictability and structure seemed so very appealing! But it also makes parents feel incapable and like they're failing their babies. The reality of the stress I put myself through while trying to force my tiny human into these one-size-fits-all routines was anything but. I vividly remember my attempts to get her to sleep without cuddling her: standing hunched over her cot with one hand on her chest (with juuuuust enough pressure and oh so still) and shushing until I felt dizzy. She did actually fall asleep this way… after — I kid you not — 30 minutes of doing this. And she was up again 15 minutes later. That's time *not* well spent!

By all means read about sleep for education, suggestions and reassurance, but don't let it run/ruin your life and *keep your reality in mind*. Take from any source what is useful for you and your family and happily ignore the rest. That way you get the good stuff, without the stress.

On the opposite end of the scale to gaining all your knowledge from parenting books is relying on your motherly instincts, which, if yours are strong, you should totally do. Trust yourself, your gut, your instincts, your intuition — all of it. If your sense of it is strong, it should trump all the other experts and all the unsolicited advice from strangers.

If, on the other hand — like mine — your instinct is barely perceptible, please know that this is also normal. People kept telling me to trust my instincts and I felt like I was somehow defective because I had nothing. I didn't know what was best for my baby, I didn't know what any of her cries meant (they all sounded the same to me…) and I doubted my ability at every turn. But eventually I worked things out and we hit a lovely groove of how we did things. Everyone just hits that groove at a different time. Some people fly in the baby stage, but toddlerhood was more my jam. You might find you gel with the baby phase straight away or really come into your own once there's walking and words. Neither is wrong or better than the other. We're just all different.

Out of all the things I researched and read, nothing was more helpful than an online forum of women telling me that [insert tiny thing I was worried about for days on end] was normal. And that my reaction to it was normal, too. Solidarity and community can't be beaten in those early months and outweigh book smarts by a long way.

NO GOOD COMES FROM COMPARING YOURSELF TO OTHERS

Please, please, please don't waste a second worrying about what other people are doing. I was lucky that this didn't really happen amongst my circle of new mum friends, but a weird bragging behaviour is common amongst mums, comparing and showing off about how well their babies are sleeping. My friends and I simply commiserated about how *little* we all slept – we found solidarity in our tiredness!

For what it's worth, I believe that people who tell you that their baby sleeps through at five weeks are liars. While there might be the odd one who sleeps like a log, they generally wake up a few times a night for quite some time. Some folks simply insist on outdoing others with how much sleep they're getting. It really is mostly lies, besides being unfair and annoying. And it's worth bearing in mind that some people count 11pm to 4am as 'sleeping through', whereas I definitely do not; 7pm until 7am is more like it, and we didn't get there for a rather long time.

THE 'TWO STEPS FORWARD, THREE STEPS BACK' DANCE OF BABY SLEEP

In true motherhood fashion, sleep isn't a linear progression and, just when you're getting a bit more shut-eye and think you've turned a corner, there are a few things that can throw a spanner in the sleep works.

Sleep regressions, which means more regular night wakings, even after a period of sleeping through, can happen at regular intervals. They can be brought on by a developmental leap, a change in routine or for no discernible reason whatsoever.

Teeth have an awful lot to answer for! Poor babies have no clue what's going on when all of a sudden their mouth starts hurting. Teething babies don't tend to sleep well and are grumpier during the day, too. Just as well they're extra cute once those first couple of gnashers have poked through!

Any sort of illness can unsettle a sleep routine, too. And there can be so many of those! My first started nursery at nine months old and, for the first year, she completed the whole germ bingo card and was pretty much under the weather non-stop. I remember speaking to a lovely nurse at the NHS helpline (NHS Direct at the time, now 111), so upset that my child was poorly all the time. She reassured me that I was doing nothing wrong and that this is just what happens. That was so lovely to hear! I was seriously beginning to doubt my mothering abilities.

It wasn't until she had all her teeth and had cycled through the majority of childhood illnesses that she reliably slept through – at 18 months. I hear you gasp in horror, so let me reassure you that many kids sleep through much earlier than that. My second kid was never bothered by teething pain, nor did chicken pox keep her up at night. Each child really is so different.

YOUR BABY WILL BEHAVE (AND SLEEP!) DIFFERENTLY FOR OTHERS

When it comes to other people facilitating your baby's naps or bedtime, something astounding happens – they behave completely differently.

I typed two A4 pages worth of notes for nursery to explain my baby's naptime routine with them. They followed none of it and she slept really well in a light room with lots of other babies. They honestly act differently for you than they do for everyone else, so please never worry whether your baby will be able to sleep with a babysitter or in a childcare setting. They'll be fine.

THEY'LL SLEEP, BUT NOT WHEN YOU DO

Sod's law has it that, even when babies sleep for a decent amount of hours, it's during the part of the night when you're not ready to sleep yet (7pm until 10pm maybe). And they might be done for the night by 4:30am. Those early wake-ups can go on for a while and they make the days LONG. You'll grow to love/hate/have seared in your mind forever various CBeebies shows. And very early morning walks will become your norm.

I have pictures from that time of me and the toddler baking and making Christmas cards at 5am, but we also frequently watched a good couple of hours of telly before I could function. Do whatever you can and whatever you have to to get through. The days are long. Pace yourself.

THE LENGTHS WE WENT TO TO GET THE KIDS TO SLEEP/KEEP THEM ASLEEP

* Pushed the pram for each nap for months, finding all the best sheltering places in case it rained.

* Carried the pram up to our bedroom and pushed it back and forth, half asleep, to keep the baby asleep.

* Shushing, swaying and rocking a tired baby until finally sleepy enough to place in the cot. Up to half an hour sometimes.

* Husband pushing baby for a walk for four hours in the middle of the night so I could sleep.

* Drove for so many naps. Once we drove for an hour to the seaside but were too scared that she wouldn't sleep again on the way home so we didn't even stop the car and drove straight back again.

* Making up kooky songs that kept us amused and sometimes calmed the baby. The most random one was simply repeating the director M. Night Shyamalan's name over and over to a soothing melody. Don't ask... we were tired.

* Rubbing the toddler's back and humming a sleepy song until she closed her eyes.

* All naps in the sling for the first three months for baby number two so I could have my hands free and move around to accommodate the needs of child number one.

* Stunt woman like skills of tiptoeing and crawling along the floor once baby was finally asleep. Don't make a sound and don't make eye contact!

Do I wish we hadn't done these things for fear of creating that rod for our own backs? No. In fact, I now wish we'd done more of them without feeling guilty that we were somehow ruining them and doing sleep 'wrong'. It all sorts itself out in the end, as you will see below!

THE BEDTIME ROUTINE

You're told by parenting books and courses to start a bedtime routine consisting of a bath and some quiet time in the bedroom from as early as three weeks. I'm pretty sure baby doesn't recognise it as a routine until a few months in, but I found the structure really helpful for myself. Once bath time arrived, I knew what to do and there were steps to follow, which I found very calming.

Over the years the bedtime routine for our kids has expanded and contracted, with some pillars lingering to this day:

* Bath, then quiet time in the bedroom, fed to sleep then transferred into Moses basket/cot.

* Tried a glowing seahorse that was meant to be magical. Turns out it played the German national anthem (I'm German; hilarity ensued), but didn't help with sleeping. There is now all sorts of tech from shushing sheep to contraptions that mimic the motion of a moving car. Sleep is big business!

* Tried to get them attached to a soft toy or a dummy. Neither worked.

* Weaning off breastfeeding to sleep, gently, over the course of weeks.

* Swapped feeding to sleep for rubbing back and humming a song.

* Talked to the toddler about going to sleep by themselves because there was now a baby to look after, too. It worked!

* An uncountable amount of trips to bedrooms for a wee/drink of water/itchy toe/feeling hot or cold/nightmares, etc.

* Used a sleep consultant when my second was ten months old. She was up every hour and it was breaking us. Someone stayed overnight with us and it was the best money we ever spent (if you're thinking of going down this route, please do your research into who you are using, as this is not a regulated industry. We did not use any form of crying it out).

* Adding white noise/blackout blinds/nightlights to their rooms.

Both kids (at five and nine years old) still have blackout blinds (actually Velcroed to the window frame), a night light and white noise on while they're sleeping. Those were the big turning points for us and we don't dare alter anything, just in case! And the white noise is actually super handy at blocking out fireworks, barking dogs, early morning birds, etc.

ASK FOR HELP

First things first — it's outrageous how little sleep humans can function on. You might get up some mornings, convinced that you can't make it through the day, but you will manage, again and again, no matter how bone-tired you are. That's a fact. But that doesn't mean that you shouldn't ask for as much help as you can to ease the sleep deprivation, because being sleep-deprived affects you in lots of different ways, some fairly extreme, others building up over time. Your temper can most certainly shorten, you might crave carbs like nobody's business for that boost of energy to get through the day (crisps and carrot cake for me!) and you might feel rather foggy in the brain department. Every mum has a story of putting the kettle in the fridge or putting a takeaway coffee cup on the car roof and driving off.

At the time, you'll think you're actually doing OK, until you get some sleep again. Then, looking back, you'll realise how totally not OK you actually were.

SHARE THE LOAD

In my case, being sleep-deprived amplified my anxiety so much that we eventually decided my husband would get up with the kids in the night once I'd finished breastfeeding. It absolutely makes sense that the one who deals better with tiredness takes on a bit more of it.

If you live with someone who you're sharing parenting responsibilities with, don't both stay up at night when the baby is awake. We made that mistake at the start and it's not a good tactic. I remember us both being up for hours trying to settle the baby to sleep, resulting in us both being utterly shattered. For the first few weeks with my second, my husband and I slept in shifts. Baby was having trouble settling (her digestive system taking a while to kick in we think) and needed to be on someone to sleep. So we'd take it in turns to be with her for two hours while the other one slept in our bed.

DON'T FIGHT THE NIGHT

It's hard enough getting up numerous times; don't add misery to it by counting how often you got up or chart how long you've slept.

We wasted a lot of energy getting upset with each other for how we were coping in the depths of the worst sleep deprivation. I cried a lot and my husband would get cross and punch a pillow. Then he came up with the following mantra and it remains my favourite parenting motto to this day: *What happens at night, stays at night.*

We did whatever we had to to get through the night without hurting the baby, ourselves or each other, and in the morning we wouldn't mention it. We'd see it as a new day and a clean slate and simply carry on. It lifted a huge weight and was honestly a turning point. It didn't make the nights easier as such, but it removed the feeling that we had to behave a certain way to be doing a good job. Just getting through it was enough. No judgement, no holding back. It comes back again to being a team (see page 30).

MAXIMISE THE SLEEP YOU DO GET!

While a full, uninterrupted eight hours may be elusive for a little while, there are things you can do to manage your sleep deprivation in the meantime. There'll still be moments when you'll feel so exhausted you're not quite sure how you'll change that next nappy, but trust me, you'll do it.

Remind yourself that this won't last forever and have a look through the suggestions below to take the edge off and boost the sleep and rest you *are* getting.

GET INTO BED EARLY

Be in bed for eight hours (at least) and allow yourself to relax. In lieu of an uninterrupted eight hours' sleep, get into bed as early as you can, even if you're not sleeping. Rest, read, cuddle a child, even watch TV (as controversial as that may be), but get into bed. Mentally, you'll feel like you've had more sleep and you can maximise the time you're actually sleeping because you'll already be in your pyjamas when you feel sleepy/once the first night feed/waking is done.

Sleep before 12am is the most rejuvenating, so try to get to bed as early as you can to get some quality sleep in, even if it's broken. You might miss out on some time with your partner, but it won't be forever and it will make surviving this season of your life so much more bearable. Even doing this a couple of times a week can have a massive positive impact on your health and vitality.

ENJOY JUST RESTING

Even when you're struggling to go to sleep or anxious that you'll wake up again shortly, by focusing on getting the best quality rest you can, you are making the best of a challenging situation. Nice deep, slow breaths while relaxing your whole body as much as possible go a long way to restoring yourself, even without nodding off (totally beneficial in the middle of the day, too!), as does giving into gravity and letting yourself get as heavy as possible. Taking this one body part at a time is really useful and often has the effect of lulling you to sleep, since your mind isn't thinking at top speed about hundreds of other things.

And if your mind simply won't let you rest and relax, you could try following a guided meditation or a sleepcast designed to help you nod off, or simply focusing on enjoying the sensation of being in your bed.

Whatever you do: **Don't count how often you got up or how many hours you've slept.** All you'll do is think about it way too much and end up feeling even more tired. I used to keep meticulous track of how many wake-ups we'd had and how much sleep that amounted to for me. All it did was make me grumpy, angry, anxious and more tired. And you know what? You've made it through every single day so far and you'll do it again, no matter how much sleep you've had. And you'll do it again and again!

HAVE A WIND-DOWN 'ROUTINE'

Do you have a bedtime routine for yourself to help you feel sleepy? I'm guessing probably not much, beyond watching telly and brushing your teeth. In an ideal world, where the time after the baby has gone to sleep stretches ahead for luxurious hours, you would not use any electronics for at least an hour before going to sleep, write a to-do list for tomorrow, journal about the day and any thoughts that have cropped up and meditate. You might have a warm bath with some essential oils and read a book for a little before drifting off. Maybe once the kids have moved out, right? I sometimes don't even wash my face before going to bed I'm that exhausted...

However, what you can do is find small things that signal sleep time for you that don't require you to find extra hours in the day – your 'Mummy wind-down' if you will. A few effort-free suggestions to simply signal to your brain that the end of the day is approaching and that it's time to slow down include:

> ✳ a cup of herbal tea while reading
>
> ✳ lighting the same candle every evening, which over time you'll start associating with bedtime
>
> ✳ focusing on your breathing as you're going to sleep, letting it slow and deepen and relax the muscles around your body as you breathe out (see page 79 for some gentle breathing exercises)
>
> ✳ thinking about what went well today/what you'd like to do differently tomorrow (awesome to turn down an anxious mind)
>
> ✳ setting an intention for the next day
>
> ✳ using a hand or foot cream, ideally with a nice smell to it

AVOID CAFFEINE IN THE AFTERNOON

This is fairly obvious, but caffeine, even relatively early in the day, can affect how well you go to, and stay, asleep at night. If you're sensitive to caffeine, don't consume it after 12pm; if you think you cope OK with caffeine, make that 3pm.

GENERAL SLEEP HYGIENE

There are loads of things that are proven to enhance the quality and quantity of sleep you're getting. However, lots of them are not particularly suitable for people with young babies, so here are the ones that you might still be able to implement to get the most snooze out of your 'head on pillow' time:

> ✳ *Make it as dark as possible.* Blackout blinds or curtains are great.
>
> ✳ *Keep the room cool.* Again, this makes for a more restful and deep sleep. (Although I love to be really warm at night, so, once again, do what works

for you!)

* *Use an eye mask and headphones* if you're able to, to really block out the world and help you to remain asleep once you've dropped off. This can be especially nice if you're feeling a little overstimulated from the day — block everything out, to really relax. Even if you do this just until the first wake-up of the night, it might make a real difference to how rested you feel.

* *Use a blue light filter* on your phone in the evening. Blue light is harsh on your eyes and can disrupt your circadian rhythm, which will make it more difficult to fall asleep. You might find that your phone has an eye comfort setting or you can download blue light filter apps. TV emits blue light also, but I'm not about to tell you to curb your evening or night-time TV watching. That would just be cruel. If you find that your sleep is really disrupted or you can't drop off, there are blue light filtering glasses you can get if you want to get geeky around sleep.

HOW TO COPE WITH EXTREME TIREDNESS

First of all, be extra kind to yourself. Being tired makes you feel foggy and emotional, and everything feels at least 15 times harder. Go easy on yourself and cut yourself lots of slack (I'm not sure I've included that phrase enough in this book!):

* *Rest whenever you can.* Have a nap or simply lie down and close your eyes for ten minutes. Or lie on the floor with your feet up the wall for a few minutes – this is surprisingly rejuvenating. It all helps, even if it's just to boost you through the next couple of hours.

* *Physically go slower.* Simply acknowledging that you're tired and moving more slowly lets your brain know that you're listening to your needs, even if you can't fully meet them.

* *Get some fresh air.* It'll help refresh you, lift the fog a bit and you might even get to chat to another adult as an added bonus.

* *Stay hydrated.* Dehydration and tiredness is not a good combo. I've always found iced, sparkling water gives me a bit of a lift.

* *Breathe.* Deep and slow. Your breath really will nourish you and create

that little bit of extra energy and patience whenever you need it.

* *Call a friend.* Venting about how tired you are can be quite therapeutic.

* *Eat.* Being exhausted is not the time to deprive yourself of food. And sometimes (or a lot of the time...) a slice of cake or packet of crisps is what'll carry you through to the end of the day, and that's OK.

> *'Sleep has so many variations to the "norms" so don't compare your baby to others. Sounds obvious but it really isn't!'*

> *'Make noise when baby sleeps — don't creep around the house (so they don't wake at the drop of a pin)!'*

THE GIST

Do whatever you need to do to get through each day and night. You won't be sleep-deprived forever.

KATIE PALMER

INFANT SLEEP CONSULTANT

I don't think anyone fully prepares you for the realities of sleep deprivation with a baby. Some people deal better with it than others, but I don't think anyone would describe it as a walk in the park. I think we all want the manual that tells us the secret formula that will make our child sleep well, but the reality is far from that. However, there is a science behind sleep that applies to all babies and maybe if more parents knew about it, we'd feel a little better prepared.

1. Babies are not born knowing the difference between night and day. This develops in the first 15 weeks and is known as our 'circadian rhythm'. This helps our body to produce melatonin which is the sleep hormone. For it to be most effective, we need to make the most of the daylight hours. Routine helps with this; it doesn't need to be super strict but having a consistent start time to your day and regularly timed feeds (every three to four hours) all play a vital part. The same with the bedtime wind-down – it tells our brain it's time for sleep.

2. Research shows that babies have the ability to self-settle from five weeks. This does not mean sleeping through the night, but they can start to link sleep cycles together and sleep for a few hours at a time. This is something to be aware of, but also savour the moment. If you are enjoying those sleepy baby naps with your baby snuggled up to you that is completely fine. Only make changes as you feel ready, and every parent is going on their own journey which may be different to yours.

3. We naturally wake several times a night as we transition between sleep cycles. It's completely normal. As adults we wake around five times

a night and it can be much more frequent for young children. The biggest change is at around three to four months when your sleepy newborn starts to wake up and become more aware. If they need help to fall asleep, they will look for that help more in the night. As your child learns to self-settle, they can start to join these cycles together and sleep for longer stretches.

4. There will be a lot of talk about sleep regressions, but there isn't research to support these. Our children are ever-developing and learning. Each day is something new and sometimes these things will blow their mind, and this can affect sleep. If you have a good sleep time routine in place, you can support your child through these changes with that familiar consistency. That doesn't mean they won't push against those sleep time boundaries, but they find reassurance in the familiarity.

5. There is not a one-size-fits-all approach, and everyone is on their own journey. Some people struggle with the sleep deprivation and want to get their child into a routine and self-settling as soon as possible, while others have found their groove with co-sleeping. Neither is right or wrong. It's what works for you and it is only a problem if you say so. Take a moment to step back and think, 'Is this working for us?' If it is, try to block out the chatter and enjoy the moment. If it isn't, reach out for that help and know that it's OK. **If you are considering co-sleeping, it's important to be aware of the associated risks so you can keep sleep safe for everyone. More information can be found on the Lullaby Trust website: www.lullabytrust.org.uk/safer-sleep-advice.**

MANAGING MUM GUILT

You'll feel guilty about a ridiculous amount of things.

You're in control of where you place your attention and focus.

Mum guilt is annoying. And I wish it wasn't a thing, but it is. Almost a decade in, I still have moments when it gets me. The other day I cried because I'd booked a gym class that ended up impacting on a busy day and meant my husband had to do a lot more around the house than me. I mean, imagine (insert rolling eyes emoji here). He didn't mind and I *really* needed to move for my sanity, yet there I was, upset that I couldn't manage to take care of my own needs without anyone noticing. Even after years of reminding myself that I matter, and that I need to look after myself to feel physically and mentally well, the guilt still gets me. Because, deep down, I feel like I need to do it all, without effort, without impacting on anyone else, without help. Luckily those thoughts are not the boss of me (or you!) and are generally short-lived.

Mums can feel guilty about an outrageous amount of things: taking time for themselves, not keeping the house tidy enough, feeding the kids too much freezer food, not being a good-enough wife/mother/daughter/employee, going back to work/not going back to work… The list is literally endless, potentially contradictory and can contain incredibly silly things that you would have laughed at before having kids.

The good news is that it's not an entirely useless emotion and might be pointing towards something in your life that feels out of alignment or that you're not completely happy with. Sometimes you can do something about that and sometimes you can't. Either way, it's useful to look at guilt (and any emotion for that matter) as information. Information that you can ignore if it's appropriate, but information none the less.

A little guilt is normal and healthy. It lets you know that you care enough about something (in this case parenting) to want to do it as well as possible.

Let's have a look at where mum guilt might originate from, followed by some suggestions for nipping it in the bud/acknowledging it and moving on.

EVERYONE FEELS IT; COMPARISON FUELS IT

If your guilt pops up through *comparison* with others (maybe they're parenting differently, taking more time for themselves, have a cleaner home), ask yourself: what do they have in place that you don't? Family help? More childcare? Different priorities? Own *your* choices and circumstances. You do you. Stop comparing as much as you can. And it helps to remind yourself that no one has it all together and all figured out. Some people are just better at pretending! More on comparison in the next chapter.

LOWER YOUR STANDARDS

What if your guilt is *self-imposed*? Maybe you have impossibly high standards for yourself that you're trying to uphold while having small kids. If this is you, it's time to get lowering that bar. Lower. Lower still. Lower. Now you're getting close!

You can't possibly keep up pre-child standards across the board. You don't have the same amount of time, so it doesn't make sense. So once again, pick what's important to you and cut yourself a whole lot of slack for the rest. Head back to Chapter 3 (page 41) for help with working out your priorities.

IGNORE THE CRITICS

Has your guilt been brought on by *comments* from others — maybe their *judgement* about you working/not working or your parenting choices?

Remind yourself that this is more of a reflection on Judgey McJudgeypants than yourself; they are deflecting some of their own issues on to you. You don't have to accept this — it's not your baggage to take on board.

YOU MATTER

If it's guilt around self-care and taking time for yourself, do you deep down feel like *you don't deserve to treat yourself well*? This was me for the longest time. I needed my husband to practically force me to have a rest/get away from the kids for a while, because I just felt too guilty for needing a break. How irrational is that? Very! But very common. Let me remind you again that you matter, and that you are worthy of care, attention, time and space for yourself.

IS IT ALWAYS GUILT?

We often slap the label of 'guilt' on to an emotion if we're simply not sure what we're feeling or if it's an uncomfortable emotion we can't quite put our finger on.

When you decide to meet friends for a drink and hand over the bedtime routine to a partner or a babysitter, you might feel icky because it's the first time you've done it and you know things won't get done your way. Sure, you could label that as guilt, but could it also be a sense of not feeling in control? Or simply being out of practice with taking time for yourself?

And when you've lost your temper with someone near and dear to you (including your kids!)? That might well be guilt you're feeling, but in this case its purpose might be to alert you to the fact that this is a way you don't want to behave. You can then use that emotional nudge to assess how you could handle a similar situation in future or avoid it occurring in the first place.

Guilt isn't always necessarily a bad thing. 'But how do I use guilt in a positive way?' I hear you shout? Don't fret, there are some handy suggestions below. Try the one that resonates most first and go from there.

ACKNOWLEDGE THE GUILT

Let that guilt steer, rather than shame, you. (In case you were wondering, the difference between guilt and shame is this: feeling guilty means you've done something that you're not keen on and it's making you feel a bit iffy. Feeling shame means that you view your whole self as bad, defective or wrong (which is never, ever the case, so stop that right now please and thank you).)

Don't ignore your guilt or push it deep, deep down and pretend it's not there. It will bubble back up when you least expect it. Instead, notice it and think about whether there is something you need to do to address it. If your guilt is fuelled by a situation that you're no longer happy with, this is your indicator to do something about it.

FEEL THE GUILT AND DO IT ANYWAY!

Again, acknowledge that the guilt is there, but just practise doing the thing you're feeling guilty about anyway. This is especially important if you are feeling guilty around taking time for yourself. I used to feel so guilty about going to the gym and either leaving my toddler in the crèche or with my husband, but the more I did it, the more I appreciated the benefits that the exercise brought me, so it got easier and easier. Practise, practise, practise making time for yourself and pushing through that guilt.

LAUGH

You've got to, because the whole parenting thing is pretty bananas. If you catch yourself feeling guilty about something silly (we've all done it), laugh it off.

FOCUS ON WHAT YOU ARE DOING WELL

Instead of stewing in guilt about stuff that you perceive other people to be doing better, bring to mind some stuff that you do really well – like reading bedtime stories, giving cuddles, being creative, singing silly songs, etc. Whatever you feel you are doing really well as a mum, or a person, make *that* your focus. Because what you focus on expands, and what you try to ignore is all you can think about (like polar bears, once someone asks you not to think of polar bears). So acknowledge the guilt as outlined above, but then let it waft off into the sunset.

LESS GUILT, MORE AWESOMENESS

Feeling guilty takes up a *lot* of energy. Imagine what that energy could do, focused on something useful!

TAKE SOME ACTION

'Action over anxiety' is one of my favourite mottos. 'Action over guilt' also applies. Do something, anything, to move you away from and dissipate the guilt. Physically get up and move your body. This works super well to reset yourself in all sorts of circumstances. Or if you've worked out that the guilt is pointing you towards something that needs to be changed, take one tiny action to get you started straight away. Let's take losing your temper and shouting at your kids or partner as an example. You could remove yourself from the situation, sulk and feel bad, and then pretend that it never happened. Or you could take some deep breaths, apologise for your outburst and explain what led to it (in less detail for kids, obviously). Maybe you can even think of ways to avoid future outbursts together.

TALK IT THROUGH

This could be with a mum friend who gets it and can lend an empathetic ear, or with your partner, who more than likely has no idea about the many shades of guilt that are darkening your mum experience. They might not understand exactly where you're coming from, but it really helps to increase mutual understanding getting these things out into the open.

'Look after yourself first and foremost — you are important too. Shower every day if you can, rest and don't feel guilt!'

'Ask for help. Don't just accept people's offers, but dictate exactly what you need without feeling bad, guilty or like a failure.'

THE GIST

Guilt isn't entirely useless, but it will morph out of control if you let it. Acknowledge it, deal with it if necessary or let it go and move on.

AVOIDING COMPARISON

Motherhood looks different to everyone. Everyone has massively different circumstances and expectations. Some have lots of family to help; others might have the cash to pay for help while you don't. It's deeply unfair and impossible to compare ourselves to others and their reality, yet we all do it. While this is very natural and normal (we all want to do our best and comparison helps us assess where we fall in our perceived hierarchy), it can become problematic when we value what others have above our own situation. Which is why I think it's so important to give yourself time to work out what's realistic and of value to you within your given circumstances, then keep your blinkers on, focus on your own life and enjoy what you have as much as you can.

Social media has a lot to answer for when it comes to comparison with other mothers. Where once upon a time you had your antenatal group to compare yourself to and maybe a few people in your neighbourhood, there's now a limitless amount of people at your fingertips to seemingly measure up against.

Luckily, the tide on the Interweb is changing a little and you'll be able to find many posts and accounts that are keeping it very real indeed. But for every one of those, there are another 20 that are hyper-filtered, super-curated accounts of some kind of motherhood fantasy. Don't look and definitely don't compare.

Unfollow everything and anyone whose posts make you feel less than good, even if it's friends and family. If their posts, opinions or general outlook are upsetting you or are causing you to spend valuable headspace thinking about how you could/should do things differently, then they've got to go or at least be muted.

GOOD-ENOUGH PARENTING

Here's the thing: your mothering or parenting doesn't have to compare to what anyone else is doing. All it has to be is 'good enough' for you and your family. That's right — good enough. Not perfect. Your baby doesn't need a 'perfect' mother, whatever that even means. Chasing an idea of perfection can actually become very harmful for your physical and mental health if it means you'll exhaust yourself trying to meet some ideal or standard that you've set for yourself (or has been set by the media or other comparisons). More than likely, you'll never meet that ideal anyway, which will add frustration and low self-esteem on top of the exhaustion — not a nice mix I'm sure you'll agree.

Good-enough parenting covers all the important bases of keeping the child loved, cared for, safe and fed, but there's no need for fancy bells and whistles. The term and concept is based on the findings of Donald Winnicott, a British paediatrician and psychoanalyst, and has actually been around for decades — society has just largely ignored it in an effort to be more and have more all of the time. Let's put a stop to that, shall we?

Pick the things that are important to you (as previously covered in the book and touched on again below) and let everything else simply be good enough. Maybe you get a kick from decorating the nursery to Instagram perfection, but don't enjoy baby classes so hang out with your mini me at home. Maybe you thrive on putting on make-up every day to feel put-together, but only cook from scratch once in a blue moon. Maybe your baby food is all organic and home-made, but the last time you dusted you weren't even pregnant yet. It's all good (enough).

Letting good enough be good enough is honestly one of my greatest victories in my parenting journey. Being able to shrug and say to myself 'meh, that's good enough' and being able to move on without giving it another thought is priceless. Having energy and headspace left over for myself at the end of the day is what keeps me a (mostly) happy mum for my kids. If I was run ragged every day (like I was for the first two years), my temper would be shorter, I'd stress eat, drink more, and feel frustrated and resentful all the time. That's no way to live and no way to model motherhood to our kids. I don't want them to grow up thinking that motherhood is this endless chore that swallows up your identity and instead show a way of parenting that models less self-sacrifice through rejecting the concept of perfection.

CHECK BACK IN ON YOUR PRIORITIES

With comparison in mind, you could go back to the start of the book and look at the section on priorities again (page 41). Once you know what's important to you, it matters way less what other people are doing.

If, for example, someone's posting about a beach holiday with two kids under five and your worst nightmare would be getting on a plane with your kids (and emptying sand out of nappies), then there's no point in feeling jealous, is there? Just remind yourself about what's important to you and your family and keep focusing on that.

'Remind yourself that babies are little people. People are all different — likes, dislikes, temperament, personalities, how much they eat, sleep, move... everything. Babies are small versions of this and none of them are the same. While it's interesting to see what other people are doing, don't bother trying to do the same or fit a mould. Focus on what's right for you and your baby. And if you don't know what's right, just do what feels right and you will figure it out.'

'When tempted to compare, know that some other mums lie, for some unknown reason — they present their perfect self, which makes you feel rubbish, as opposed to their likely reality.'

'Just put no pressure on yourself. Your family and circumstances are entirely different from every other family out there. Give yourself time to figure out what works best for you and don't worry what anyone else is doing.'

MILESTONES, SCHMILESTONES

Babies will do things in their own time, so try not to let other mothers/babies, or even the health visitor, stress you out. This makes total, logical sense, yet I know that it is incredibly hard to do. It was quite the surprise to me to find out that I appeared to care deeply that my baby was slow to roll and crawl, and the sense of pride I felt that she was an early talker was totally over the top. Of course, there can be developmental delays in kids that are important to notice, but don't worry. You absolutely won't miss anything important, but you don't need to watch your baby development app like a hawk and worry about baby not sitting up or crawling by a certain date.

THE GIST

Unfollow anyone who makes you feel less than fabulous about your parenting (and your life). Be clear on what's important to you and stick to that.

ELA LAW

INTUITIVE EATING COUNSELLOR AND NUTRITIONIST

You will have been inundated with helpful and not-so-helpful advice around food and eating, probably since before you even got pregnant. Pregnancy can be a tricky time in terms of body image and, while this is covered more thoroughly in Chapter 7, what and how you eat can be significantly impacted by how you feel about your body during all stages of pregnancy and beyond.

The fact is: your body changes during pregnancy and may not ever return to the way it was. There is this huge pressure on women to get back to their 'pre-pregnancy' weight, with celebrities at the forefront of this craze. And then there is always someone in your circle of mum-mates or friends who you can compare yourself to. When these comparisons happen, it helps to pause and check in with yourself and remind yourself that everybody is different, deals with changes differently and reacts differently hormonally to this massive thing you have just done – growing and birthing a baby!

One helpful strategy is to separate body respect from loving your body. Even on a bad body image day, you can cherish and respect your body for what it has done and does for you every day. Every body deserves respect. This will make it easier for you to accept your 'here-and-now' body, even if you feel like you can't love it right now.

Now back to food. There is so much information with regards to what and how much to eat during and after pregnancy. As simple as it sounds, don't obsess about the 'healthy eating' advice too much. Yes, there are some precautions you should take while you are pregnant and breastfeeding with regards to certain foods. But a lot of the information you might get from social media posts, forums and diet gurus is unfortunately not based on scientific evidence (in general), and not obsessing about spurious advice will make you a lot more relaxed and at peace around food.

Honouring your hunger is super important at any stage of your life, and that includes when you are pregnant or have recently given birth. Now is not the time to cut down on what you eat, start a new diet, eliminate foods from your diet or lose weight intentionally. All these things cause you stress – both mentally and physically – and, with a little human to look after, you absolutely don't need any extra stress. Make sure you eat enough, eat what you enjoy and eat what makes you feel good and gives you satisfaction.

Meal planning can feel like a chore, but it can be super helpful on those days where you feel like all you have done is feed and change nappies and feed some more. Meal planning doesn't have to mean that *you* have to do the planning; your partner or a supportive family member or friend can do this for you (with or without your input). Meal planning also doesn't have to mean rigidly sticking to a certain plan; it means that you stock up on your favourite foods and long-life essentials, that you (or said family member/friend!) batch cook some meals (sauces, soups, stews, chilli, etc.) and that you make peace with the ready meal! You may even ask your support community to cook some extra and drop it round (and definitely take them up on it if they offer!).

LAST WORDS

And here we are… Throughout this book, I've shared all the things I (and hundreds of other mums) could think of that might have been handy to know before having our first baby. Undoubtedly there will be things missing, and plenty of things that will never apply to you personally, but I hope that it gives you the 'heads-up' about motherhood that I wish I'd had.

I hope you find a way of 'doing motherhood' that works for you and your family, and that you're patient with yourself while you find your groove (or grooves, as you skip through the many phases of raising a kid). Remember that it's OK to find it hard sometimes and that you don't have to enjoy every minute, no matter how many old ladies tell you so in the supermarket.

If you have any questions or would like further information on anything, my inbox is always open: *silke@raiseupmums.co.uk*. If you ever find yourself thinking, 'Hey, this should have been in that book I read', I want to hear about that, too.

Go make your own way that you feel happy with (at least most of the time…), soak up the brilliant bits that come with being a mum and knuckle through the tough bits as best you can. Whatever it takes. You've got this.

RESOURCES

CHARITIES AND LARGER ORGANISATIONS

Association for Post Natal Illness (APNI): support, education and information on postnatal illness

https://apni.org

Best Beginnings: remote support for pregnancy and early motherhood

https://www.bestbeginnings.org.uk

Home Start: Local volunteers offering support in the early years of parenting

https://www.home-start.org.uk

Maternal Mental Health Alliance: collection of local charities that offer support

https://maternalmentalhealthalliance.org

NCT: the UK's leading charity for parents

https://www.nct.org.uk

Pandas: postnatal depression awareness and support

https://pandasfoundation.org.uk

Search online for local options for: positive birth movement groups and alternative antenatal classes (Daisy Birthing and Birth Plus are ones local to me). Also search for Facebook mum groups local to you (honestly, you won't believe the treasure trove of information these places hold. Just filter out the drama and don't get sucked in — only consume what you've come for!).

SOME OTHER HANDY ONLINE RESOURCES

Mush: connect with local mums

https://www.letsmush.com

Nourish app: well-being app for mums

https://www.thenourishapp.com

Peanut: an app for women to meet for support and friendship

https://www.peanut-app.io

PELVIC FLOOR APPS

Squeezy (recommended by the NHS): the multi-award-winning app supporting people with their pelvic floor muscle exercise programmes

https://www.squeezyapp.com

Umi Health: pregnancy, postnatal and pelvic floor support

https://www.umi-health.com/

SELF-REFERRAL MENTAL HEALTH SUPPORT

Ieso Health: self-referred CBT online therapy, free in many parts of the UK

https://www.iesohealth.com/en-gb

Of course, the NHS, your GP and health visitor can also be your first port of call.

YOUR OWN LITTLE BLACK BOOK OF CONTACTS TO FALL BACK ON

Research who is who in your local area for the following (ideally before baby is born, but it's never too late really!):

Your midwife team, once you're given their number:

....

....

....

Your health visitor:

....

....

....

Women's health physio and/or Mummy MOT (for all things postnatal recovery including your pelvic floor, C-section and anything else that may need some structural attention):

....

....

....

....

Breastfeeding support (groups, 1-2-1 or a more casual café set-up):

....

....

....

....

Lactation consultant (if that's the feeding route you're choosing):

....

....

....

....

....

Postnatal doula:

....

....

....

....

....

Home help agency:

....

....

....

....

Personal trainers/group exercise that specialise in postnatal women (you'd be surprised how little knowledge there can be in a gym-run group session):

....

....

....

....

....

FURTHER INFORMATION

If you'd like to delve deeper into ideas touched on in the book, here are some starting points:

Brain upgrade during pregnancy

https://www.nytimes.com/2020/05/05/parenting/mommy-brain-science.html

Good-enough parenting

https://en.wikipedia.org/wiki/Good_enough_parent

Matrescence

Alexandra Sacks TED Talk

https://www.ted.com/talks/alexandra_sacks_a_new_way_to_think_about_the_transition_to_motherhood?language=en

Website

https://www.alexandrasacksmd.com

Motherhood Sessions podcast

https://www.alexandrasacksmd.com/podcast

NHS baby blues and mental health information

https://www.nhs.uk/conditions/baby/support-and-services/feeling-depressed-after-childbirth

NHS early motherhood health and well-being information

https://www.nhs.uk/conditions/baby/support-and-services/keeping-fit-and-healthy-with-a-baby

NHS breast- and bottle-feeding advice

https://www.nhs.uk/conditions/baby/breastfeeding-and-bottle-feeding/NHS

NHS postnatal depression information

https://www.nhs.uk/mental-health/conditions/post-natal-depression/overview

NHS postnatal exercise information

https://www.nhs.uk/conditions/baby/support-and-services/your-post-pregnancy-body

Safe sleep information

https://www.lullabytrust.org.uk

ACKNOWLEDGEMENTS

The biggest thank you and a huge huggle go to my two girls Megan and Ellie, without whom this book would not exist and I'd be oblivious to the highs and lows of parenting. Thank you for being the best kids ever and being patient with me when I say 'just one second, let me just finish writing this' over and over again.

The second biggest thank you goes to my husband who has grown with me as a parent over the last decade and has never once minimised the effort, struggle and juggle of parenting day in and day out. Thank you for being in charge of many domestic chores – it's only because of the things you take on that I had the headspace (and time) to write this book and generally stay sane. Thank you also for your thoughtful feedback on the first draft of the book and being OK with me sharing some dark and vulnerable times.

Big thanks to Claire O'Grady for creating the survey which hundreds of mothers completed and which informed so much of the content of this book (and made sure that it wasn't solely my own personal experiences). I'm so grateful to each and every person who completed the survey or weighed in on other topics within the Raise Up Mums community and across social media. It's always reassuring to know that I'm not talking into a void and that we are indeed all in it together.

Thank you Emma Jefferys, aka Action Woman, for being a source of never-ending support and forever cheering me on.

Thank you to Julia Kellaway for her editing and parenting book expertise, having been recommended to me through an act of pure serendipity! Thank you to Katie Morwenna for making me make time to create a structured marketing effort so people actually know about, and hopefully buy, the book – something I am likely to completely ignore when left to my own devices.

Thank you to Em Williams for the beautiful cover design, typesetting, general loveliness and encouragement.

Thank you to all the experts who gave their time and wisdom for this book, all of whom

I'm lucky enough to call friends. What a team to see mums through the newborn fog.

More information on each of them and how to find them below:

Sophie Burch

Sophie is a perinatal and parental therapist, coach, author, founder of the Beyond Birth guide, trainer and speaker. She's also a mum of four boys (including twins) and is on a mission to bring emotional and mental well-being awareness and practices into the lives of all parents, starting perinatally, affecting the whole family, for life.

https://www.themammacoach.com

Aishling Burke

Aishling is HCPC Registered and holds membership to the Chartered Society of Physiotherapy, the Association of Continence Advisors, Pelvic, Obstetric and Gynaecological Physiotherapy (POGP, affiliate) and the International Urogynecological Association. Her areas of expertise include pelvic health, postnatal recovery, ScarWork and cancer rehabilitation.

https://restoretherapy.co.uk

Emma Jeffery

Emma is a postnatal personal trainer and works with mums of children of all ages, not necessarily in the immediate postnatal period. She emphasises the importance of taking your time, listening to your body and knowing and accepting where you are right now: physically, mentally and energetically. Emma encourages all mums to take a graded return to movement, to shake off comparison and expectation, and to remember that rehabilitation looks different for every mum. You can work with her on a 1-2-1 basis at her beautiful studio in Hildenborough, Kent or through her online programme, The Postnatal Plan.

https://www.emmajefferypt.com

Ela Law

Ela is a non-diet nutritionist and intuitive eating counsellor. Her work focuses on supporting people in healing their relationship with food and learning to accept and respect their here-and-now bodies. Intuitive eating and body acceptance work are instruments to re-establish trust between us and our bodies, and move away from diet mentality thinking to food and body freedom. Ela uses mindfulness and visualisation techniques in her work with clients, and offers EFT (emotional freedom technique) as an additional tool to reduce anxiety and negative beliefs around food and body image.

She predominantly works with clients on a 1-2-1 basis (online or in-person). She has collaborated with local and national businesses and runs retreats and workshops on intuitive and mindful eating, body acceptance and nutrition. She has an online course on baby-led weaning – the first step of becoming an intuitive eater.

https://www.elalawnutrition.co.uk

Catherine Nabbs

Catherine is a professional counsellor and a mum of two boys. She sees clients at her private practice in Kent and online. She has a particular interest in maternal mental health and supporting women at all stages of their motherhood journey.

https://www.catherine-nabbs.co.uk

Katie Palmer

Katie is a child sleep practitioner working privately and within the NHS to help empower families to make positive changes using research-based techniques.

https://www.infantsleepconsultant.co.uk

Charlotte Tonkin Edun

Charlotte is a doula and antenatal supporter with a particular interest in birth plans and knowledge distribution.

https://www.thegoodbirthpractice.co.uk

Dr Jenny Turner

Jenny is a clinical psychologist, who specialises in offering integrative, psychological therapy to parents to support their own mental health, and to empower them to best support the mental health of their children.

https://www.mindbodysoulpsychology.co.uk

Printed in Great Britain
by Amazon

81786197R00095